THE CONTEMPORARY
ART OF THE NOVELLA

A HAPPY MAN

HANSJÖRG SCHERTENLEIB

TRANSLATED BY DAVID DOLLENMAYER

MELVILLEHOUSE
BROOKLYN, NEW YORK

A HAPPY MAN

FIRST PUBLISHED AS *DER GLÜCKLICHE* © AUFBAU-VERLAG
GMBH & CO. KG, BERLIN 2005 (PUBLISHED WITH AUFBAU;
"AUFBAU" IS A TRADEMARK OF AUFBAU VERLAG GMBH & CO. KG)

NEGOTIATED BY AUFBAU MEDIA GMBH, BERLIN

© 2009 HANSJÖRG SCHERTENLEIB

FIRST MELVILLE HOUSE PRINTING: OCTOBER 2009

MELVILLE HOUSE PUBLISHING
145 PLYMOUTH STREET
BROOKLYN, NY 11201

WWW.MHPBOOKS.COM

ISBN: 978-1-933633-81-7

BOOK DESIGN: KELLY BLAIR, BASED ON A SERIES DESIGN
BY DAVID KONOPKA

LIBRARY OF CONGRESS CATALOGING-IN-PUBLICATION DATA

SCHERTENLEIB, HANSJÖRG, 1957–
  [GLÜCKLICHE. ENGLISH]
  A HAPPY MAN / BY HANSJÖRG SCHERTENLEIB ; TRANSLATED BY
DAVID DOLLENMAYER.
    P. CM.
  ISBN 978-1-933633-81-7
  I. DOLLENMAYER, DAVID B. II. TITLE.
PT2680.E78G5813 2009
833'.914—DC22

                                    2009016785

Per Capitano,
dal Häuptling.

Fortuna caeca est
Cicero

PART I
Chapter 1

The night train rolled purposefully northward toward its destination. That's how mundanely our story begins.

The lights outside the windows of the car traced a line in the darkness that sometimes ran straight and sometimes in arcs. Seen from above, it slid through the dark landscape like a luminous snake. The man whose story will occupy our attention stood in the corridor of the second sleeping car from the front, holding a plastic bottle of mineral water which made a popping noise every time he drank from it. At first glance, he gave the impression of being younger than he really was. On the one hand, this was because his clothes fit perfectly although intended for younger wearers, but above all it was because of the upright, confident way he carried himself, suggesting that he regularly played some sport. And yet This Studer (the name of the man we shall accompany on his journey) is an inactive, even a lazy person who would rather not move at all. And if we look more closely, his forty-eight years are clearly evident.

Otherwise, there's nothing special about him. Shall we try to describe him anyway? He's one of those people whose appearance is hard to recall precisely, even though his face is actually not an ordinary one. Or is it? At most, you remember the protuberance on the bridge of his nose, his bristly sideburns, or the fact that he's tall and powerfully built and leans slightly forward when he walks, like a ski jumper about to launch himself from the takeoff platform. Certainly the most noticeable thing about him is his smile. It's probably the cause of the lines and wrinkles that fan out from his eyes like a corona. Or do we only imagine those wrinkles, those scars of cheerfulness, in our recollection of him? There are people who can't stand this smile, which is neither feather-brained nor fatuous, who react to This Studer with coolness or even annoyance. They feel he's putting them on, laughing at them, even mocking them. What's that guy smiling about? they wonder. Does he know something I don't? Why are things going better for him than for me? A person who's always in a good mood is a challenge; someone who's always smiling, a provocation. What could be worse than another person's happiness? Not that his unhappiness would make us happy, but we need it in order to bear our own.

Train stations and villages flew by outside the windows. The landscape had long since sunk into darkness, the night sky barely bright enough to distinguish it from the horizon. Far away, the soft line of a hilly ridge stood out against the reddish glow from the town beyond as if cut from paper. Now and then, the lights of a remote farmhouse would rush through the black space, and when the cars crossed a switch point, they creaked as if the train were going to break apart.

This Studer loved traveling by train. It lifted him out of time and gave him a chance to let his thoughts wander aimlessly hither and yon. He was so lost in thought that he didn't notice the man who had stepped into the corridor from another sleeping compartment until he was standing next to him and started talking.

"Can't get to sleep either?" the man asked.

"I'm not tired."

"I'm always tired. But I can't sleep anyway."

The man took a flask out of the breast pocket of his sports coat and wagged it back and forth in invitation.

"Want some?"

This Studer shook his head. The man's eyes were filmed over with moisture; perhaps he had been crying. The protruding bulge of his brows merged into a receding forehead and gave him a hounded look. Outside the windows, the lights of a new housing development flew past.

"Come on! A little swallow never hurt anybody."

The man unscrewed the cap that also served as a cup, filled it, and handed it to This Studer.

"Schnaps?"

"Grappa. Go ahead, try it!"

The fiery liquid ran down his throat and spread a pleasant heat through his chest and stomach.

"Warms your heart right up, doesn't it?" asked the man, taking a healthy swig himself.

The door at the end of the long corridor slid open and a group of Japanese came toward them. All the men wore identical dark blue suits. The women, whose dresses also seemed more like uniforms, modestly lowered their gaze and did their best not to come into contact with the two of them as they squeezed past.

"They're everywhere nowadays," said the man after the group had left the car.

"They don't bother me."

"Me neither. But they're everywhere anyway, whether it bothers you or not. Japanese! They all look the same."

"Just like us."

"You traveling on business?"

This Studer nodded. He didn't particularly like talking about his work. "Jazz trumpeter" sounded pretentious and affected, didn't it? It was easier to talk about the music lessons he gave or enthuse about his three or four really talented students. He was a good trumpet teacher because he wasn't really a teacher. He didn't know how to teach, but he did know how to ignite a passion for the trumpet and keep it burning. He taught his students to connect every tone to some memory as the way to short-circuit right through to their feelings. What's more, he was a good teacher because he never gave the ones with no talent a false sense of hope.

"Let me guess: you're an architect! You're on your way to Amsterdam because someone has chosen your design. Am I right?"

"I'm a musician."

"An artist! What'd I say? May I ask what instrument you play? You don't look like a singer."

"I'm a trumpeter."

"A trumpeter! Classical? No . . . hang on a sec! You play in a dance band."

"I play jazz."

"Just as I thought! An artist! I could tell right away."

"I don't know that I'd call myself an artist . . ."

"Are you going to perform in Amsterdam?"

"A friend of mine has a quintet. His trumpeter got into an accident . . ."

When the pianist Henk Scharpenzeel, a friend of many years, called to say that his regular trumpeter Kees van Dijk was in the hospital with a broken wrist from a motorcycle accident and did This have the time and inclination to play a week with his quintet in the *Kapitein Bird*, Studer had said yes immediately.

"And where are you performing?"

"In a club near the station."

"Does it have a name?"

"The *Kapitein Bird*."

"Well, I don't care too much for jazz, but now that I've met you . . . ! When exactly are you going to play in this *Kapitein Bird*?"

"All next week. How about you? What do you do?"

"Me? I'm a sales representative. Cosmetics. We sell beauty cream, youth cream, hand cream, foot cream, and face cream. Cream for wrinkles and dark circles under your eyes. I sell lipstick, body lotion, and baby powder. But right now I'm on vacation. Do you know the Hotel Krasnapolsky? My wife, of course, has no idea it's right next to the neighborhood with the ladies, if you know what I mean! You're traveling alone, too, I take it?"

"No. I'm with my wife."

"Your wife! You lucky dog! Love is a fairy tale."

"And in fairy tales," said This Studer, ". . . in fairy tales everything is possible."

Chapter 2

His wife Daniela lay on her back in the lower bunk, trusting and vulnerable, arms spread out, the blanket kicked to the foot of the bed. When he squatted down next to her, she opened her eyes.

"Where were you?"

"Kerosine Budnitz was keeping watch over you."

"Kero . . . isn't your name Gasparus Gasparius today?"

"It was until ten minutes ago. But for the last ten minutes, I've been Kerosine Budnitz. He's been standing guard over you."

"Standing guard?"

"Protecting you."

"Where are we?"

"Somewhere in Germany."

"You gonna get in here with me?"

"I don't think there's any way you can avoid it."

"Then I'm in luck again."

"Absolutely. We can rent out the other bunk."

"Good idea."

"To a young woman, a redhead with . . ."

"To that young conductor!"

"I could get into the top bunk!"

"Or I could!"

"Let's both do it and rent out the bottom one!"

"Just get in here, would you?"

He got undressed, clambered over Daniela, snuggled up against her back, and put both arms around her. Then he pushed her hair apart as if opening a curtain and kissed the back of her neck with its delicate film of perspiration.

"Tomorrow I'll show you where they make the best *poffertjes* in Amsterdam."

"I don't like *poffertjes*."

"You're going to love these."

"What's your name again?" she asked drowsily.

"Budnitz."

"And your first name?"

"Kerosine," he said and pulled the blanket back up over her.

"What a stupid name."

"You said it!"

"Pleased to meet you anyway, Kerosine Budnitz."

"The pleasure's all mine. By the way, I sell all kinds of fuel. If you're interested, you know where to find me."

"Fuel? I'm so glad to hear it."

"Are you on your way to Amsterdam too?"

"Mmm, perhaps," she murmured. "We'll see."

In a moment, she was asleep again. He pressed his face against her hair and inhaled the smell he loved more than anything else in the world. Sometimes it was in his nose even when he was far away from her. Smells have no name so we've got to resort to comparisons to describe them. That's why we don't forget them, why our sense of smell is the best custodian of our memories. Daniela's hair smelled of vanilla and summer, even in the spring when the rain poured down for days and a cold wind swept the last snow from the sidewalks. The bunk wasn't just narrow, it was short, too, and his feet touched the cool windowpane. Every story has a beginning, of course, but we remember the beginning of a love story with particular pleasure and clarity, don't we? On the permeable border between exhilarated weariness and sleepy excitement, This Studer saw himself once again entering the pottery studio in Ftan. He's twenty-eight and playing three gigs in the Engadine with his band *Torso*. They've already played in Sils and Pontresina. Tonight they're appearing in Scuol. From the paintings of Flemish masters, we know the light that fills a potter's studio: fox-brown, golden, a light from when the world began. For a business trying to sell things, it's surprisingly dark in this vaulted room. Nevertheless, the bowls, tureens, cups, and plates standing on the shelves of unfinished wood shine so intensely he's compelled to touch them. Their colors and glazes are extraordinary. Even he can see that, though he knows nothing about the business of a potter.

One particular cup the color of a summer sky in the mountains is so delicate he is surprised he can't see right through it. It is made of nothingness, contains nothing. Is it even permitted to drink from it? And what would you drink? Air? Light? Isn't it made to play music instead, inaudible music? He's got to have it. He doesn't notice the young woman sitting at a little table in the corner until she clears her throat.

"This is the most beautiful cup I've ever seen."

"I've made ones even more beautiful than that."

"How much is it?"

"What are you going to drink out of it?"

"Don't know yet."

"Coffee?"

"Do you have something against coffee?"

"Not at all. But maybe my cup does."

"I'll probably keep it with my favorite things."

"It's a teacup."

"I don't like tea very much. How much is it?"

"What's it worth to you?"

"I don't know yet."

"Are you on vacation in Ftan?"

"I'm in a band. We're playing in Scuol tonight."

"What kind of music do you play?"

"Jazz-rock."

"Rock?"

"More jazz than rock, actually."

"What instrument do you play?"

"Trumpet."

"I can't stand jazz. And trumpet . . . well, I think trumpet is just dreadful!"

Her hands are much too big, must belong to some other woman. She's got dirt under her fingernails, which are trimmed short. Her wool pullover is full of holes. She's barefoot and wears a toe ring made of two interwoven bands of silver. He falls in love with her on the spot. And she with him. He can see that, even though at the time he had no experience with women.

And what of the cup? He paid thirty francs for it back then without batting an eye, even though he thought the price shamelessly high. For a long time, the cup stood in the bookcase next to his other favorite things, among stones and shells from vacation trips, his very first mouthpiece, and the ticket for a Miles Davis concert, but for the past few years, it's had the place of honor on the windowsill of his music room, where it plays with the sunlight and reminds him of the moment he first met his wife. He's never drunk from it—neither coffee nor tea.

Later, he drifted into semi-dreams that kept slipping away one after the other, disturbed by the stopping and starting of the train, wind-blown announcements from loudspeakers, and the slamming of doors. Once, he was lying in a wooden canoe drifting down a river past fires burning on the banks, for it was night. He floated farther and farther downstream, until the canoe escaped the current and came to a stop at a bend. What might be beyond the bend, he wondered, started awake, heard the voices of other passengers going down the corridor and banging their luggage against the wall of his compartment, and let himself slip back into the next semi-dream. He encountered fish made of glass, one of his old teachers, walked along a path where nothing moved except the path itself, saw snow flurries, butterflies big as open books, and his grandfather with the dented trumpet in his lap, until at last he swallowed his own tongue. In the dream it was yellow and soft as a down pillow, so he resolved to float out of the blurry images and back up to the surface of consciousness, sat up, and looked torpidly out onto a station platform bathed in neon light and looking like a stage. The station clock hung directly outside his window showing twelve past three. A woman was standing at the end of the platform, where the darkness began. She was talking insistently to two dogs who alternately regarded her and tussled with each other, jaws agape, wagging their tails and playfully locking muzzles. Beyond the woman a silver shimmer of tracks could be seen. And then, just as the train jerked back into motion, the woman raised her walking stick and brought it down hard on the back of the smaller dog.

Chapter 3

We're looking out at the square through the dusty windows of the Centraal Station. There they are, This Studer and his wife, standing and waiting. Although the day has barely begun, the sun is already striking the top floors of buildings, illuminating towers and roof ridges. The big, wide sky is raising its sails as if to steal away with the whole city in tow. This Studer inhales the fresh air eagerly, stretches, and throws back his head. Doesn't he look like a hunter who's caught a scent? He'd probably like to fly over the roofs with the pigeons, wings spread, high up among the tatters of cloud. He laughs, flings out his arms, and turns in circles. What a day! They're in Amsterdam! He's almost bursting with energy. That's another reason why Daniela has come with him: his zest for action is contagious and frees her from her lethargy. She warms herself at his fire, and just as all colors need sunlight to bring them to life, her senses are awakened by his lust for life. For the most part, he makes her forget that she's really quite skeptical about life and sometimes finds living day-to-day so complicated she gives up in exhaustion. On certain days, however, his optimism is more than she can take. She's often reproached him for it: he should just let her feel the weariness and darkness, she whom the wind directs and doubts assail. Her secret wish at such times is that he, too, would have his bad days.

She takes small steps forward and backward, claps her hands impatiently. She's tired, she's hungry, and besides, she doesn't like having to wait. This watches her for a while, wants to put his arms around her and lift her off the ground in his enthusiasm, but she fends him off, and he pulls a cell phone from the pocket of his leather jacket and enters a number he knows by heart. In the blinding morning light, the pedestrians who populate the Dam at this early hour are nothing but wavery lines. Are they coming toward them up the street or walking away in the opposite direction? We're too far away to hear what This Studer says, but Henk will have promised to pick them up at the train station, and now This wants to know what's keeping him.

This laughs so loud that the schoolchildren crossing the square turn to stare at him. The telephone conversation lasts less than a minute. He grabs their two bags and his trumpet case and looks around for a taxi. It's only the beginning of April but already warm as summer.

"Come on! Kerosine Budnitz is gonna treat you to an order of *poffertjes*!"

We have an image of ourselves we want others to have too. We want to please, to be accepted. Henk Scharpenzeel has never wondered what other people think of him. He's not interested in how others see him. Where we try to fit in, he does what he likes. Today he was wearing form-fitting black tights like a trapeze artist, a jeans vest, and a slouch hat. His feet were encased in a pair of yellow inline skates. The way he skated bespoke the former speed skater: his left hand rested on his back, his right arm made generous pendulum swings, and his legs moved so deliberately he gave the impression of moving more slowly than he actually was—a slim black figure in a sixteenth-century painting, gliding across a frozen *gracht*.† We can see that at this tempo, he could keep going for hours without slowing down, serenely following an invisible path without bothering about the crowds in Vondel Park. This and Daniela were sitting in the spring sunlight at the Café Vertigo by the Film Academy. Henk coasted up to them with joyful yelps, oblivious as a singing child. He got a kick out of the appalled face Daniela made. He was familiar with this expression from his own wife Marjoke. She couldn't stand it when he did something that embarrassed her. This ran toward him with outstretched arms and lifted him off the ground in a hug. Daniela is not a jealous woman, but there are moments when she envies her husband his friendship with Henk Scharpenzeel. It has always been an easy one and time has not been able to weigh it down with unnecessary baggage. With a single gesture, they can call to mind some past episode and unleash a storm of laughter that brings all conversation in their vicinity to a halt. At this moment, for example, This made a face and pretended to play a guitar and Henk could immediately picture them in the apartment they shared in Boston more than twenty years ago. Their living room window looked out on a commuter rail bridge where, for some reason, trains often stood waiting before continuing on into the station. In summer, they opened the window, turned Jimi Hendrix or Larry Coryell up to full volume, and played air guitar for the impatient passengers ready to faint from the heat, putting on a show they wouldn't soon forget. Sometimes they really played for the people their wild trumpet and accordion

---

† **canal**

version of some jazz standard, dissolving even the grimmest faces into grins and putting entire cars in a party mood . . .

"Sorry I didn't pick you up. Marjoke needed the car."

"You can make it up by paying for my wife's breakfast," said This, pushing Henk into a chair. "And now tell us what you've been up to!"

The playground and sunbathing lawn were being renovated, so parts of the park were fenced off. Some teenagers had set up camp on a grassy area by the water, stretching ropes between the branches of a low-hanging tree and draping colorful blankets over them. Light batik dresses hung from a line, billowing in the wind and then going limp again. A girl with hair so thick and long it looked like a hand-knotted carpet sat between two boys, playing with an orange that shone in the sunlight.

They had almost reached the bridge that leads across the water to the Emma-Laan when Daniela let go of This's hand, ran to the edge of the canal, sat down in the grass, and pulled off her shoes and socks. A building on the far bank had its own dock, a tongue of boards extending far into the reeds. The surface of the green, almost blue water, was absolutely still, giving the impression that the canal was deeper than it probably was. Tufts of eelgrass trapped below the surface opened and closed in the invisible current like hands moving in unimaginably slow motion.

"Nobody will find us here," said Daniela.

"Nobody's looking for us!" said Henk indignantly.

"There you go!" laughed This.

"Because we're not in Amsterdam at all," said Daniela.

She rolled her jeans up to her knees, stuck her bare feet into the turbid water that seemed to swallow them up, and gave a little scream.

"Where are we then?" asked Henk.

A tree trailing its scrawny branches in the canal leaned so far over the water that its roots could barely keep hold of the ground anymore. A piece of the embankment had washed away; the water had broken off a bite with its large, soft mouth. Sunshine filtered through the canopy of leaves and glittered on a raft of duckweed floating close to shore. This saw the gooseflesh come up on his wife's calves and disappear again, like condensing breath. When she pulled her feet out, the muddy water had left two delicate rings above her ankles, a stocking hem of slime and algae to be washed off.

"Where are we then?" Henk repeated.

"On our island," said Daniela.

"Which I have built," This explained.

"Of mud," said Daniela.

"And pencils and matches," This quickly added.

"And cardboard and paper and glue."

"Without water?" asked Henk.

"With water, of course," said Daniela, sticking her feet back into the water and wiggling her toes.

"*Is het niet te koud?*" called a voice behind them.

The man was at least eighty and stood on a clump of scorched grass. He wore a coat that was surely much too warm and leaned on a cane. His face was ravaged and lifeless, but his eyes beamed with enthusiasm.

"*Is het niet véél te koud?*" he asked again.

"Yes, much too cold, but marvelous!"

She pulled her feet from the water and held them up as proof. Her face was relaxed, carefree, and This would have liked to take her narrow feet with their dark-red painted nails in his hands and warm them up. Then he saw the smiling face of the old man standing behind them. In whatever time was left to him, he would recall this moment: *Isn't it too cold?* The stranger's cheerful face and her feet gleaming like fish in the morning sun. *Isn't it too cold?* Her slim calves with water dripping from them. *Isn't it much too cold?* The wriggling, tanned female feet as they disappeared into the armpits of the man sitting next to her, who cried out since the feet must have been ice cold, but still looked at the woman full of admiration and then hugged her to him.

A gust of wind shattered the surface of the canal into a thousand glittering shards and passed through the trees like a wave, bending all their crowns in the same direction until they righted themselves again. Branches groaned wearily. The tops of the tallest trees floated like clouds above the impenetrable green of Vondel Park, while the bushes whispered as if deep in conversation.

Chapter 4

Henk Scharpenzeel's guest room was a cube of glass set atop the house on the Sophialaan that his wife Marjoke had inherited from her father a few years ago. Filled with light and sparsely furnished with a bed, a table, chairs, and a leather sofa, the room led out onto a terrace that looked down on a pond connected to the lakes and canals of the Vondel Park. A window above the tub in the blue and white tiled bathroom had a view out across jumbled rooftops toward the center of the city. As This Studer pushed their bags over to the wall, he spotted a record player next to the bed with a stack of LPs leaning against it.

"Would you like some music?"

"It's probably all jazz!"

"Think so? Then you don't know Henk very well."

This sat down on the bed and flipped through the albums.

"Dave Brubeck, Thelonious Monk, Herbie Hancock, Jean-Luc Ponty, Les McCann, Dollar Brand . . ."

"See? Nothing but jazz!"

"Patience, patience!"

He laid aside Chick Corea, Keith Jarrett, and Duke Ellington, and finally waved a cover in the air triumphantly.

"Here you go! Frank Zappa! *Hot Rats* with Captain Beefheart."

"You're kidding!"

"Or what about The Who, *Tommy*? The Stones, *Sticky Fingers*, with the zipper cover by Warhol? Santana, *Abraxas*—my very first LP. *Meddle* by Pink Floyd. Or this one: Johnny Hallyday! You always want to go to France on vacation, right?"

"Has he got any new stuff?"

"You're going to like this one for sure! Close your eyes."

"Oh, come on. I'm tired."

"Exactly! Close your eyes. Please?"

Daniela stretched out on the sofa and closed her eyes. He took the LP out of its sleeve and put it on the turntable. Before Paolo Conte had finished even the first line of the song, she was back on her feet and pulling This up too. She wanted to dance. Isn't it wonderful when we know exactly what the person who shares our life is thinking and seeing in their mind's eye? "Un Gelato al Limone" brought back a sun-drenched square, a bar with a jukebox and a tin café table on which were two espresso cups and their hands reaching for each other. This and Daniela had driven his Renault R4 via Cremona, Parma, and Modena to Florence for two weeks. In this bar in Fiesole, This ordered a lemon gelato for Daniela and then pressed the button for Conte's song in the cover by Lucia Dalla and Francesco De Gregori. Then he'd asked her to dance.

"But this isn't Lucio Dalla!"

"No, this is the original version!"

She pushed him away without letting go of his hand, then twirled back up against his chest.

"You danced better twenty years ago."

"What would I do without you!"

"You'd just have somebody else!" said Daniela and kissed him on the nose.

"Remember what else we did that day?"

"After the gelato, or before?"

"After."

"In Florence?"

"No, in Fiesole!"

"The same thing we're going to do now," she said.

She shoved him backwards onto the bed and bestrode him, tensing her calf muscles so he lay between them in a tender vise. Her face was glowing; you could read the desire in her eyes.

Later, he sits in a chair by the window and watches her wake up and yawn. His trumpet is beside her on the bed. Where the skin of her ankle is especially translucent—almost transparent—he can see an artery beating with energetic regularity, as if to draw attention to itself. Whorls of light tremble on the parquet floor.

"You were talking in your sleep," he says.

"What about?" she asks, stretching both arms above her head.

"About me, of course! Shall we give Anna a call?"

"I'm sure she's quite happy to be left alone for two days."

"Just to let her know we got here all right."

"She doesn't care!"

Once again, he is taken aback by how prickly Daniela can be about their daughter. Two years go, shortly before Anna's fourteenth birthday, she had metamorphosed into a snappish young lady who treated her parents as though they were personal enemies she was friendly to only when she wanted something from them. Earlier, Anna had called Daniela "Mom": "Mom's my best friend." Now she calls her "Daniela" and considers her a rival. It seems only yesterday that she wanted Daniela to wash and dry her hair for her; now she locks herself in the bathroom for hours on end. First, she forbad them to call her "Annie" in front of other people, now she insists they always address her as "Anna." Her moodiness often makes her mother livid. Can't Daniela recall her own puberty? Didn't she too withdraw and detest everyone else because she couldn't make peace with herself? Or is it just that This is able to live with his daughter's ignoring him most of the time because of the occasional moments of intimacy between them, when Anna chooses to cry on his shoulder instead of his wife's? And why does Daniela have to let Anna sense at every opportunity that she can't stand her boyfriend Sebastian (who wants everyone to call him "Bashi")? This himself doesn't know what to say to a seventeen-year-old with gigantic hands and feet who's two heads taller than he, always has a slight sweat smell, and studiously avoids all eye contact. But he accepts him as his daughter's boyfriend.

When This was sixteen, he almost gave up jazz and the trumpet. He wanted to play guitar in a rock band. What had persuaded him to continue? The album *A Tribute to Jack Johnson*, where Miles Davis proves it's also possible to play the trumpet like *this*; his father's remark, "About time you stopped playing that nigger music"; and his grandfather, who instead of taking him to task just gave him a quiet smile and put on "Nuff Said" by Ben Webster.

"OK, so we won't call Anna," he says.

"I feel so lazy," said Daniela, squinting. "So lazy."

I'm helpless against it, he thinks: this desire for her, still there after all these years—this lust.

"I gotta go. We're rehearsing at two."

"So lazy, it's criminal . . ."

He can't help himself. After all this time. He takes the trumpet off the bed and lies down next to his wife. Set me on fire; consume me. Her skin is hot and flushed. She smells like a teenager. She still knows how to excite his curiosity. It's easy to think of her as a stranger, the woman without a name, and to desire her again and again.

Chapter 5

The number 2 streetcar took the tight curves of the Koninginneweg with surprising speed. This Studer stood at the back of the car, near the conductor he'd bought his ticket from. The heavy-set, uniformed woman sat on a high stool in a little booth, absorbed in a paperback novel. Nevertheless, when they approached a stop, she pulled the microphone to her mouth with the assurance of a sleep-walker and without so much as raising her eyes, announced the stop with a cheery voice: Valerius. Emma-Straat. Cornelis-Schuyt-Straat. Jacob-Obrechtstraat. She reminded This Studer of earlier times and the conductors of his childhood. He had grown up near the last stop on a streetcar line, where the tracks looped around an allotment garden. A Tessiner named Martinelli had leased the plot. He bred rabbits in a hutch, slaughtered them, and sold them to people in the neighborhood. "Who'd want to eat that stuff, anyway?" grumbled This Studer's father, "Goddamn wop!"

Every time he said it, This's mother would respond, "Martinelli's not from Italy, he's from Bellinzona!"

Smoke rose from the chimney of Martinelli's garden hut day and night. He loved making fires and every few days would burn leaves, branches, or trash. If the wind was from the wrong direction, the smoke hung between the houses and the whole end of the streetcar line was fogged in.

"He only keeps that garden so he can burn his trash," This's father declared.

Martinelli's garden hut, tool shed, tomato plants,

vegetable and flower beds lent this obscure suburb the air of a rural village. The lot where Lumpert's trucking company was located gave the neighborhood a bedraggled, almost wild feeling. Lumpert's wilderness was their paradise, their reservation, where the rules of parents and teachers didn't apply. Patches of stinging nettles proliferated between tumble-down wooden sheds. Worn-out truck tires and empty gasoline drums were piled along the entrance drive, and the fences and waist-high brick walls that divided the loading docks were collapsing. In daylight, the property had a cheerless look, but when it got dark, it was transformed into a place they walked past quickly with their eyes cast down. They would never have dared go in there at night, but during the day it was their favorite place. They only had to manage to slip past Lumpert's guest workers. The shed under whose roof they had set up their camp was used to store trucks and almost no one ever came in there. Sunlight fell through the chinks between the boards and made bright stripes on the floor. Here they smoked cigarettes, drank wine, had masturbation contests, talked about their parents and siblings, and kissed the girls they couldn't look in the eyes when they were on the playground. The tracks passed right behind the hideout, not three yards away. This loved the sounds the tram made, the screeching, singing, groaning, creaking. Some cars knocked and hammered as they got underway. Others were almost silent. He could tell the new power cars from the older ones and knew by their sound exactly how far away they were and when they would reach the end of the line. When it rained, the sounds were brighter, harsher, as if amplified by the water. If there was snow on the ground, it sounded like a heavy sledge sliding along the tracks, sneaking into the terminal for a well-deserved rest. If the overhead wires were frozen, sparks sizzled and bathed the square in front of the shelter in an

unreal light. The very first test of courage This Studer had
to pass was to jump onto the coupling between cars before
the driver closed the doors and started off. The first few
times, he'd jumped off again after a few yards, just like the
others, but before long he would run along beside the second car when it was already moving and wait to jump onto
the coupling until the tram was about to outdistance him.
For three summers, the longest ride was to stay on around
the entire loop and not jump off until the tram turned into
the Püntstrasse. But one day Martinelli's oldest son Luciano just stayed put, squatting on the coupling, and they
ran after the car all the way down the Püntstrasse until the
tram, with Luciano grinning on the coupling, turned into
the Albisriederstrasse and disappeared in the direction of
town. Luciano was back again in the second outbound car, a
proudly beaming victor who even enhanced his new record
by sneaking onto the return tram without a ticket.

The coins they put on the tracks to get flattened were
their favorite currency for trades at school. They also put
caps—they called them "ladies' farts"—water balloons, and
paper bags filled with dog shit onto the rails. They gave the
passengers a good scare and made the drivers swear at them.
One of them even stopped his tram, got out of the car, and
chased them all the way to the edge of the woods, shak-
ing his fist at them. In winter they hunkered down behind
piles of snow-covered tires on Lumpert's property and
threw snowballs at the windows of passing streetcars. The
heads of the startled passengers jerked forward, back, shot
upwards or ducked down between the rows of seats like the
heads of marionettes whose puppeteer has gone mad.

This Studer idolized the drivers who stood around
in front of the shelter, stretching their legs and smoking
cigarettes. They joked with the housewives carrying their
groceries home and made them laugh. Some women were

there at the terminal every day and their laughter echoed in his dreams. Until he was fourteen, This wanted to be a streetcar driver. He sat on the kitchen table all afternoon long and practiced regulating his speed with the antenna of the transistor radio on the widow sill. It pivoted back and forth just like a driver's steering lever. He drove with his eyes closed, imagining which part of the route he was on so that at the right moment, he could announce the name of the stop into his microphone and bring the tram to a stop without the least jolt: Albisriederhaus, Freilager, Dennler-strasse, Hubertus, Crematorium. He pictured the passengers to himself, children on their way to school, retirees with dogs, office and factory workers heading for the Siemens factory. And of course, housewives with shopping bags who liked his voice so much they forgot to get out at their stop and stayed in the car to the end of the line.

Pursing her lips, the heavy-set conductor called out "Spui."

This Studer got out and let himself be carried along across the square by a swarm of tourists. A strong gust of wind carrying an odor that reminded him of Martinelli's brush fires blew hats and caps off peoples' heads. This looked around for the jazz club where he would be playing the next five nights.

Chapter 6

They rehearsed all afternoon. *Kapitein Bird* occupied the ground floor of what had been a granary, its windows barely three feet above the water of the Uilenburgergracht. After a while, This had the feeling that the bottle-green water was reacting to their jazz: when they played quietly, it lay smooth as a mirror in its stony bed, but as soon as they picked up the tempo, its surface was broken by little ripples that got choppier during solos and gave This gooseflesh on his forearms.

They hadn't all played together before, so they went through the whole set. It took them about half an hour of cautious playing to get to know each other, then suddenly the moment arrived—in the middle of "Trane's Blues"— when they meshed like five gears. This could feel a collective sigh of relief run through the quintet. The face of Willem, the earnest bassist who couldn't have been more than twenty-five, broke into a happy grin—you could tell he couldn't help it—and the drummer Tim Krabendonk let out an enthusiastic whoop.

They lost track of time, forgot they were only supposed to be rehearsing. After the saxophone solo on Brubeck's "In Your Own Sweet Way," they started a long improvisation that didn't stop until Connie, the club's bartender, came and sat on the edge of the stage to smoke a cigarillo. The *Kapitein Bird* would be opening soon. There were less than two hours until their first set. They packed up their instruments and strolled over to the Nieuwmarkt. Henk knew a place in a side street the tourists hadn't discovered yet. They crowded around a small table and ordered beer and toasted cheese sandwiches.

"You're almost as good as Kees," said the young bassist in accentless German and quickly glanced away from This.

"Thanks," This replied.

"Kees," said Henk with a laugh, "is a walking disaster area. He's nothing but trouble. This, on the other hand, This is . . ."

"*This is een geluksvogel*," Tim Krabendonk finished his sentence for him, "fortune's darling, a happy man."

"Only ignorant people can be happy!" Now the bassist's voice was shrill. How quiet it had suddenly become!

When was the first time someone had called him lucky? His best friend Andreas was in love with a girl named Marianne who told him she'd never kiss him. Why not? Because she was in love with This. "You're just a lucky dog," Andreas had told him and gone looking for another friend. How old had he been? Nine. Eleven years later was the first time he'd thought of himself as lucky. He was in a bus with the drummer from his first band, Desert Air. They were in Norway, on their way from Oppdal to the Molde Jazz Festival. The bus skidded off the coastal highway and overturned. He was the only person in his row of seats to survive. But was he really luckier than other people? No, he just handled it in a different way. Too soon, too late, so many missed opportunities—you've got to recognize luck when you see it. He has a lot of friends who waste time waiting for a miracle that will redeem them, transform the life they perceive as a melancholy pencil sketch into a richly-hued oil painting, friends blind to moments of happiness while waiting for that miracle to arrive. What's more, you've got to be able to stand being lucky. Many of his friends do everything they can to destroy it because they're sure that fulfillment could be worse than failure. They're driven by the conviction that nothing is more like hell than heaven, that heaven exists only until they get there, or comes into existence only once they've left. They're not convinced that something was right until it's over. This laughed and raised his beer glass.

"*Prost*," he said, and clinked glasses with Willem who lowered his eyes in embarrassment.

"Anybody can be happy these days," said Arnold Leupen, "just ask your doctor, Willem! Prozac makes even a dim bulb shine!"

"This doesn't need any medication to be happy," declared Henk.

Happiness? What is happiness? A sudden, unexpected attack that makes you forget life's burden? A rapture lasting whose concentrated expression was turned inward. Wasn't music supposed to have the opposite effect, make you lose your inhibitions, become euphoric, express your innermost feelings? Over the years, she realized that jazz did indeed reveal his inner life, namely, inside the cheerful and contented This, a contemplative and melancholy man awaited his turn to speak and tell about himself.

At that concert in Scuol, it took him a long time to notice her. When he finally caught sight of her standing way at the back beside the exit, the tone of his playing changed, turned bossy, argumentative, almost shrill, lost all its warmth. This wanted to impress her but got so excited he dropped the microphone while making an announcement. She didn't like the band's music. It was aggressive and cold. It sounded like six men out to prove how fast they could play. This didn't calm down until after the concert, when they lay holding hands in an unmowed meadow and smoking the hash she had brought back from Morocco, nothing in their field of vision but a myriad of stars and dark, silent cliff faces inching towards them, falling back when they blinked, then rushing toward them again. Her pulse pounded against the tips of his fingers resting on her sturdy wrist. They lay there in the meadow until the light began to flare above the circle of mountains in the east and the sun illuminated the highest peaks. He didn't return to the lowlands with his band. During the four days she spent with him, Daniela felt lighter and more at ease than she ever had with a man before. Life at the side of this man had less weight. It seemed brighter and more auspicious. The four days fairly flew by. They spent every minute together, but she still managed to get some work done. He sat in her studio, watching her in silence. Not even that had disturbed her. He helped her empty the kiln, carefully picking up each cup and admiring its form. He didn't touch his trumpet once during those four days. He fit into her life as if he'd always belonged there, even though she'd never planned to share it with anyone. What was he up to with her, this man who always had a smile on his face as though he found life amusing, a lazy river in which he floated along without a care in the world? When she took him to the train station in Scuol, he'd asked if she wanted to go to Tuscany with him. She hadn't really gotten involved with him yet, but was already wondering if she would ever be responsible for making that smile disappear from his face . . .

In the meantime, the sound of his trumpet had become the beloved root tone of her daily life. Yet she was always astonished by its effect on his audiences. They became soft and docile, allowed him to impose emotions on them and inveigle them to change their mood. Over the years his tone had become warmer and fuller, his playing leaner and more reticent, his pauses so perfectly timed they created the illusion of complete spontaneity that was the soul of jazz, as he had explained to her. He would often play a note as if himself surprised by its sound, as if he were correcting a mistake. Although his playing was tentative and fragile, his tone was confident and powerful. So his solos sounded like delicate speculation rather than obstinate assertion, but always clear and assured. They were over before you even realized they had begun. He made himself small in his playing yet drew attention to himself, and this slight irritation was felt by his listeners, made them aware of him.

Daniela still didn't care much for jazz, but the audience in the *Kapitein Bird* was eager and insatiable. They played longer than they had contracted for, as if in a trance. They didn't want to stop, couldn't stop, not yet. At the end, they played three Chet Baker tunes: "We Know It's Love," "Looking Good Tonight," and "Blues For a Reason." This felt like he was floating a hand's breadth above the stage. He could sense every fiber of his body, every muscle, although he was light as paper. Willem held his bass in an affectionate embrace. They had captivated the audience, held them between their teeth the way a mother cat holds her kittens, and shaken them gently back and forth. Everyone was grinning, everyone was happy, and it was their doing. If they stopped playing, it would all come apart at the seams. If the magic spell evaporated, life would engulf them again, so they kept on playing, just one more song, really just one more final song before the encores, Miles's "Four," because you should stop when you're at your best. His grandfather had taught him that.

Backstage it's so constricted they get in each other's way. They start jostling, shoving back and forth.

"If I was still smoking, I'd smoke one now!" Arnold shouts. He tears open the window and sticks his head out.

The wall above the mirror is papered with postcards from all over the world. A broken drumstick lies on the window ledge.

"Your solo in 'I Fall In Love Too Easily' was worldclass," says Willem and thumps This on the back.

"Don't any of you old codgers smoke?" shouts Arnold. "What is this, a band of goddamn retirees?"

Henk hands Arnold a bottle of beer, lights up a cigarette, and blows smoke in his face.

"Thanks, that's better! Much better! What're we playing as an encore again? 'Decision' right? Is that what we agreed?"

"If you weren't so damn good, I would have thrown you out long ago, Arnold!"

"So you really are the boss after all? Put your prostheses back on and let's go, dudes. I wanna play some more!"

Chapter 8

The large windowpanes of the Indian restaurant were fogged by the heat from the kitchen. The lights outside along the canal melted into blurry smears. Drops of condensed moisture were strung along the metal molding above the door like a sparkling garland, reflecting the colored bulbs over the entrance.

They were the last ones in the place, but the owner had assured them they didn't need to hurry. After performances, This was always as keyed up as an over-tired child and so ravenous that he ordered all sorts of things even though he knew his appetite would be satisfied after a few bites. Although Daniela had often seen him in this state, it was always fascinating to watch the way his eyes shone and he said anything that came into his head while helping himself to the various little platters, bowls, and plates that covered the table. There was mango chutney on his chin and his ears were glowing. Daniela herself had experienced this feverish state only as a child: when they finally got to the hotel in Spain after eleven hours in the car, she would be so tired she couldn't keep her eyes open, yet much too excited to fall asleep. When she worked in her studio, however, she was enveloped by peace and serenity. It was like watching herself in a dream, without having to think about it, as she gave shape to a lump of clay on the potter's wheel.

"Were we good?"

"You were great!"

"You think Anna's eating enough?"

"Your daughter, Madame Anna, wants to lose weight," said Daniela.

"But she has to eat something."

This tore off a big piece of naan, shoveled a few forkfuls of okra onto it, and shoved it into his mouth. A sign on a taxi roof swept past, a yellow streak gliding across the window pane. The owner came over to their table to clear away the empty platters. This gave him a inquiring look, and he reassured him with a wave of his hand.

"Don't hurry! Don't hurry! Where are you from?

"Switzerland" They both answered at the same time.

"And you?" Daniela asked.

"The Netherlands," the man answered proudly.

"You were born here?" Daniel asked.

"No, Delhi. Not here. *Sie sprechen Deutsch?*"

They nodded. The man wore leather shoes with no socks. He smelled of curry and beads of sweat stood out on his forehead.

"You like jokes?"

They nodded again. The wind rattled the awning so hard its poles banged against the window and made them all jump.

"What's the difference between India and Europe?"

They shook their heads. The owner wore a heavy silver chain on his wrist and he kept stroking it unconsciously, making it writhe like a snake.

"Your gods ride on donkey. Ours on tiger!"

The man burst out laughing and disappeared into the kitchen without waiting for their reaction, the soles of his shoes smacking the tobacco-colored linoleum.

"Our saxophonist Arnold? His wife left him. You know why? Because she couldn't stand the way he ate. Can you believe it?"

"So how does Arnold eat?" asked Daniela.

"'If I have to watch you chewing just one more time, I'm going to kill you.' That's what she said."

"Are you bothered by how I eat?"

"I love watching you eat," he answered. "Do you mind the way I brush my teeth?"

"Since when do you brush your teeth?"

"His wife said she only stayed with him because she was afraid of being alone."

"She must have been bored."

"With Arnold? Are you bored?"

"Bored? With you?"

Her hoarse laugh could still send shivers down his spine. The down in the little hollow between her ear lobe and her neck shimmered in the neon light and trembled slightly as she shook her head.

"And you," she asked, "are you bored with me?"

"And how! I'm just about dying of boredom."

"How come we're still together then? What do you think?"

"Because it's cheaper? Or because I don't feel like moving again?"

"I'm serious, you meathead!"

"Ever heard of something called love?"

"Other people stay together because they're afraid."

"Or have no imagination," he added.

"I'm with you because you let me live my own life."

"I sure do."

"And you don't do it just because you're afraid of losing me otherwise."

"No? How come, then?"

"Because you're a generous man."

The owner hummed as he dried glasses. The two cooks had gone home. The fire still burning in one of the three tandoors cast a red light onto the tiles. This waved his empty beer bottle back and forth.

"Shall I get us two more Kingfishers?"

Daniela nodded. The restaurant didn't have a liquor license but the owner had recommended a package store around the corner that carried Indian beer.

"Put your jacket on. It's raining," Daniela called after him, but This was already out the door.

She could hear the wet flapping of the mop as the owner swabbed the tiled kitchen floor in rhythmic strokes. The ceiling fan blew his hair every which way and he kept pausing to smooth it down. The pane of the window onto the back courtyard was painted black and an empty wire hanger dangled from its latch. When Daniela turned back toward the street, a shadow had appeared outside the fogged-up window, the outline of a man with horns on his head, horns that wiggled back and forth. Suddenly, a face was pressed against the glass, a flattened nose, and Daniela saw it was This.

"Your husband: very funny," the owner called from the kitchen and pointed at This who was rolling his eyes, holding two beer bottles up to his head, and calling out something she couldn't understand.

This pays the cabbie, a black man with thick rasta braids, and immediately plunges into the underbrush bordering the pond of the Sophialaan.

"What are you doing?" Daniela calls after him.

"Gotta pee!"

"But we're almost there!"

"I can't wait, gotta go now!"

Trash trails from the bushes like tinsel, the ground is strewn with crushed soda cans and fast-food packaging. This groans with relief as he frees himself of the beer. Most of the houses are dark. Here and there, TVs are on. Nearby, someone is making a racket with his bicycle bell. Clouds are spread above the Vondel Park like an open fan, their undersides illuminated by the lights of the city.

He buttons his fly, yawns, and suddenly feels dead-tired. Only then does he catch sight of the man lying under the bushes. He's wrapped in a wool blanket with his head cushioned on a rucksack This at first takes it for a stone. He starts toward the man to see if he needs help when he spots the dog sitting just beyond in the underbrush, as if standing guard. The dog is large but so emaciated the ribs stand out beneath his dirty brown-and-white brindled coat. There's a spot over one eye that looks like an eye patch and a festering wound across his chest. This is so startled he catches his breath. They stare at each other without moving. A thick root has broken through the dry earth and sticks up between them like a barrier. This raises his arm, but lowers it again when the dog reacts with a loud growl. Slowly, holding his breath, This starts to back away . . .

Chapter 9

At fourteen, he falls in love for the first time. When the French teacher leans over him from behind, her breasts almost touching him, he gets dizzy. He wants to turn around and press against her. Sometimes her red hair tickles him while she erases one of the verbs he's declined wrong and he can smell the cigarette she smoked on her break. Her jeans are so tight they outline the triangle between her legs as clearly as if it was the topic of class discussion. One day he sneaks into the teacher's lounge. Her locker is labeled in a handwriting he doesn't like. It's unlocked and empty except for a paperback edition of Albert Camus' *L'Étranger* and a bright blue umbrella. He's considering whether to keep the balled-up tissue he discovers on the floor of the locker when he spots a butt in the ashtray. Its filter carries the exact half-moon lipstick imprint of her mouth. He sticks the butt into his pants pocket and steals out of the room. In the days that follow, he touches the butt cautiously with the tip of his tongue over and over. He shivers, closes his eyes, and licks it, rolls it gently back and forth between his lips like the French teacher does in the schoolyard when she's lost in thought and believes no one is watching her.

If the class is taking a test, she sits on the edge of her desk with her legs crossed and gazes out the window in boredom. The top leg bobs up and down. At some point, she slips her heel out of the shoe with its wedge-shaped cork sole and lets it dangle for whole minutes at a time from the toes with mother-of-pearl polish on their nails. It's impossible for him to concentrate on the test because he's memorizing every detail of her body and imagining how her skin must feel, how she smells, and how she would writhe at the touch of his boyish hands. He senses that she knows he's watching her. Aren't they accomplices?

Daniela runs her fingers through her hair, twists it into a shimmering knot, lifts it up and weighs it in her hand, exposing the bright hollow of her neck to the light. With dilated pupils she regards herself in the mirror, twirls stray strands, lets her hair fall back, and then makes a single braid held together by a brooch and pin.

He sees the soft curve of her shoulder and the bone that protrudes at the end of her shoulder blade. Her skin shines. She's taken a long bath and smells of coconut milk. The thought of his fingers gliding over her body and opening the tiny buttons of her summer dress makes him sigh with yearning. She turns around and shakes her finger at him.

"So? Who am I speaking to today?"

"I don't know yet."

"Kerosine . . . what was your last name again?"

"Budnitz. But that was yesterday."

"And today?"

"Today? How about Oleg Poleg?"

"I don't like it."

"Kalle Bärenschleifer?"

"The guy from the storybook?"

"No, the one from the blue forest where women disappear."

"I don't like that either."

"The name, or the forest?"

"Neither one. How about Grochsus Kahn?"

"I always find my own names!"

"Just as you wish!"

"Today I'm Saccharine Saccharus!"

"The pharmacist?"

"No, the tour guide!"

"Whatever you say."

"Saccharine Saccharus is going to show you Amsterdam, if you have no objections."

"But I know the city much better than you do!"

"Exactly!"

The first place he takes her is a back courtyard in Jordaan. The yard is paved with rounded cobblestones that shine with moisture from a recent shower. The rear building is covered with scaffolding and draped with a yellow tarp that billows in the wind. Next to a board fence separating the courtyard from the next property there's a bench and a rosebush. Henk had brought him here the last time This played with him in Amsterdam. A former piano student of his lives on the second floor of the front building and he's fallen in love without telling her about it. Henk knows that her neighbors allow her to practice every day from eleven to two, and he sometimes stops by to stand under her window and listen in secret.

This wipes the bench dry with his hand and they sit down. There are smells of coffee and freshly baked bread. The window in the second floor is closed.

"What are we doing here?" asks Daniela.

"Patience," answers This, putting a finger to her lips.

In a few minutes, it's eleven o'clock. Musicians are disciplined people, This Studer knows. Two birds hop to the edge of the gutter and swoop off toward the ground. Their shadows sail across the tarp. What if Henk's former student is on a trip or moved away? The stained-glass windows of the stairwell—ivy and tulips—gleam in the sunlight. Somewhere there's a clatter of dishes. A girl laughs and a man scolds her, but the next moment bursts out laughing himself. Then someone opens the second-floor window. This sees a hand, a bare arm. He doesn't see the woman's face and Henk didn't describe how she looks. Her first notes sound uncertain, even harsh, as if she didn't really want to play. She hasn't found herself yet. She's fighting the piano instead of entrusting herself to it. He can hear her fear of the instrument, a fear he's familiar with. But soon, her touch becomes assured, the notes flow one into another, woven into a carpet you want to stretch out on with your hands clasped behind your head, relaxed and free.

"Is that why we're here?"

He nods. The courtyard acts as a resonating chamber, amplifying the notes, giving them power, volume. The chords seem to be almost palpable in the morning air. Daniela puts her head on his shoulder. Now the music is a torrent, a hurricane.

"She's good. Do you know her?"

"How do you know it's a woman?"

"No man plays like that. Do you know her?"

"I don't, but Henk does."

"Schumann," says Daniela, '*Kinderszenen.*'"

She closes her eyes and turns her head toward the window, as if the music were a source of warmth. A sharp wedge of sun falls into the courtyard, dividing the tarp on the scaffolded façade into a light and a dark half.

"You don't even like classical music."

"But you do."

"Thank you, Saccharine Saccharus."

"My pleasure."

The Café Bern is a run-down place that's so cozy more than a few guests use it as their living room. This and Daniela get a table by the window through which they can watch what's happening out on the Nieuwmarkt. He takes the menu out of her hand and orders a bottle of white wine and cheese fondue.

"Fondue in Holland?"

"So what? You ate spaghetti carbonara in Würzburg once!"

Fondue is Daniela's favorite dish. She wants it even on hot summer days. She loves the smell of cheese and garlic. She even loves that feeling of having a stone in your stomach, a stone you have to pulverize with a couple shots of kirsch before you're able to stand up. In the café motes of dust float in columns of soft light, while outside tourists seek shelter from the drizzle. The young woman behind the bar has her hair tied up in a scarf with the iridescence of a snakeskin.

After twenty years of marriage, This Studer's conversations with his wife Daniela are as animated if they'd just met and were still courting. We don't really need to know what they're talking about. It's enough to see how they keep touching each other, how they laugh and nudge and spear bread squares for each other with their fondue forks.

The turquoise green NEMO Science Center looms up from the harborside like the hull of an ocean liner missing its stacks. They go storming through the halls without bothering to look at the exhibits. He wants to show her the view across the city and the dirty water of the former East Harbor from the roof terrace.

The terrace, as steeply inclined as a ski jump, juts out over the expressway that disappears into a tunnel beneath the museum as if it was being swallowed whole. They run all the way up to the top, the bow of the ship. This climbs onto one of the long benches and spreads his arms.

"Who am I?"

"I can't stand Leonardo," says Daniela.

"But I like Kate Winslet."

She scrambles up onto the bench, spreads out her arms, and leans into him from behind.

"I even know what you're supposed to say now."

"She is my queen of the world!" cries This, slowly flapping his arms up and down.

"Don't you want to stay longer?"

"I really can't, This. I need to work."

"Can't it wait?"

"No, it can't. You don't cancel a tour just to be with me, either."

"How about that tour to Belgium three years ago?"

"You were sick then, This!"

"Cause I didn't want to leave you!"

"I can't stay This, I really can't." The rain falling on the steamed-up windows makes the afternoon light soft, a light for one of those moments you remember your whole life. The greenhouse with the butterflies in the Hortus Botanicus is the final place he wants to show her in his Amsterdam. The heat takes their breath away. It smells of damp earth, vanilla—a heavy perfume foreign to this climate, to Europe. They are alone in the greenhouse. It's hardly bigger than their living room. He hasn't told her about the butterflies and she'll be wondering why he's suddenly taken an interest in plants, when a large white moth lands on her shoulder. Across its wings, dusted with flour, green veins meander and tail off like the lines of a watercolor. Daniela turns her head slowly toward it, so enraptured she hardly dares to move. This is how she must have looked as a girl, on the brink of bursting with joy and happiness. In the next instant, the air is filled with butterflies, crepe paper in every possible color, fluttering this way and that, rocking so feather-light they seem propelled by the mere blink of an eyelid. Then one butterfly lands on his hand, another on her head, a third on her shoulder, and they hold their breath and stand looking at one another in astonishment.

She's reserved a window seat on the train and he carries her bag in, then they go back outside. He likes farewells, wants to savor them, and that's better done on the platform. Daniela is restless. She doesn't particularly like to travel, so she frees herself from his embrace and gives him a final kiss. She will recall his smile, sitting in her studio and staring into space, listening to some quiet Schubert or Brahms, one of those melancholy sonatas that seem made for the end of the day—anything but jazz.

"Take care of yourself, Saccharine Saccharus," she says, stepping onto the train.

"You too," he calls after her.

Once she's settled in her seat she looks out the window, but he's gone, her husband. Decades later, near the end of her life, she'll recall this scene: an empty platform in Amsterdam.

Life is easy. Only the fear of it is hard.

PART II
Chapter 1

He wakes in the night to the sound of rain, a sound he always loved as a child. As usual after a performance, he couldn't get to sleep for a long time. He tossed and turned for what seemed an eternity and finally fell into such a light slumber that the murmur of the rain was enough to wake him again. The balcony door stands open and in his half-sleep, the sound of the rain seems to swell, come closer, and then recede until it's nothing but a whisper, a whisper that almost drowns out the distant barking of a dog. But the barking in unmistakable. In fact, it grows louder and more insistent, and suddenly the dog is in the room and in one leap on the bed, putting its heavy paws on his chest, forcing him down and holding him in check. This does not want to meet up with it ever again, not ever: make it disappear! But memory is not at his beck and call and the dog shakes its heavy head and snarls.

This Studer lies in his friend Henk's guest room and sees the dog before him, the dog he thought he had suppressed, buried deep in his subconscious. The intervening years rush backwards, making the animal bigger than it ever was. But doesn't memory always make small things large and large things small, transform every pond into a sea, every gnat into an elephant, the mountain into a molehill and the desert into a handful of sand?

He's ten years old when he first encounters the dog. It is summer and the wind traces patterns in fields bathed in shimmering heat. The sun falling through the leaves of the fruit trees strews points of light on the path beside the fields, a path he otherwise never takes because it's the longer way to his grandfather's house. The forest flows in velvety green down the flanks of the hills, an ocean of foliage lapping the shore just short of the first houses of town. Züst's farm is barely a stone's throw from the edge of the woods. Were we to draw this landscape, at most we might sketch in a horse-drawn wagon or a farmer at work in the fields, but definitely not what lies in wait for This. He steps into the chilly shadow of Züst's barn on the graveled area at the back of the farmyard and is brought up short, as if he had run into a wall visible only to him. He's standing in the midst of his worst nightmare, except it's real. He can't actually remember this first encounter very well, for in his memory, the dog is there from the beginning: black, heavy, with a powerful skull and dripping chaps. He realizes that the animal stands for something he can't comprehend, something that makes him terribly, terribly afraid. Did the earth tremble at that moment? Did his heart stand still? No, everything is as usual: the window above the trellised pear tree stands open. The air smells of apple tart and grass and from the meadows the clattering of the hay rake can be heard. Everything is as always, but nothing is as it was.

The dog doesn't move from his spot. He knows how long his chain is. Besides, he's patient. He knows that sooner or later, they all come closer because they can't stand his calm. They want to see him lunge at them to the end of his chain, throw himself against the bars of his invisible cage in blind rage without being able to get at them (or so they think). He knows that when people stop to look at him and shudder, their curiosity will get the better of their fear. They will step nearer—too near. This boy is no exception. Back then, This Studer sensed instinctively that the animal would show him something he hadn't been aware of: his own evil side. But at this first meeting, he simply stands at a safe distance looking at the dog. The chain would have to be at least twice as long. He stands there, thunder-struck, frozen, turned to stone, sees the swarm of gnats dancing above the dog's skull, the saliva dripping onto the gravel from his black-speckled chaps, sees the gigantic paws which—inexplicably—he wants to stroke, sees the dog's gaze. It is that gaze he will never forget, sleepy yet wide awake, mild yet aggressive. Is such a thing even possible? Can one and the same gaze be that of both a friend and a foe? Is it not astonishing that he can stand up to and return that gaze? They face each other without moving.

Later he stood leaning against the open balcony door, looking up at the stars. The street and pond below were bathed in blue moonlight, the magical light that has saved so many lost mariners and misled so many dreamers. Life, he thought, does not shrink from repeating itself. There seem to be things that won't leave us in peace until we've really comprehended them.

Try as we might to catch it, the moment of falling asleep always eludes us. When we attempt to recall our dreams next morning, sometimes we can and sometimes we can't. And even when we can, there's always a remainder we can't resolve, a disquiet that shows us we've forgotten something, some little detail indispensible for seeing the entire picture, the whole dream.

In Paradise, thought This, it must always be early morning because that's my favorite time of day. He placed a bare foot onto the terrace but winced back at the ice-cold shock of the wet tiles. The sky was pallid and washed-out, as if covered by a fragile skin, a membrane so delicate a breath of wind would suffice to tear it. It was still early. In this residential district at least, Amsterdam was not yet awake. It seemed to This that the city and its inhabitants were waiting for their cue to begin the day. He slipped into his shoes and walked out to the railing. The sidewalk was deserted, hardly a car could be heard. The buildings looked like pencil sketches that could easily be erased. Now the light was changing swiftly, becoming stronger and brighter, the sky no longer just a scrim stretched behind the city. Was this now the ultimate color of an April day? The water of the Sophialaan pond was like glass, mirroring the wall of trees. A boy was walking along the shore and windmilling his gym bag through the air. He was taking his time, but you could see he was heading somewhere.

Chapter 2

His grandparents' house was a half-hour walk from his parents, in a clearing in the woods overlooking the city. Shortly before one reached their garden gate, the path went past a little building that housed a transformer and was always buzzing like a swarm of bees trying to escape to freedom.

The garden gate was painted white, as was the iron fence. In the summer, flower heads nodded over its pointed posts. Despite his grandfather's regular oiling, the gate always squeaked. Beyond it, a flagstone path led through a garden that over the years had literally outgrown his grandparents. After his grandmother's death, it had gone irrevocably to seed, becoming again part of the forest on the other side of the fence.

His grandfather was a cabinet maker and the shop where in his best days he employed seven workers was located at the far end of the clearing. He parked his lime-green Opel Kapitän next to the shop and used it only for outings with his wife. Although his grandparents' house was less than a stone's throw from the joinery, it was so overgrown with bushes and trees that his grandmother never noticed her grandson slipping into the shop every day as soon as school was out. The floor of the building was covered with yellow shavings and the smell of wood, resin, and machine oil hung in the dusty air. This loved the whoosh of the planes, the screech of the band saws and milling machines and the patter of the sawdust against the board walls as it spewed from the sanders. He loved the murmur of the carpenters' talk as they bent over their work and he tried to remember the jokes and sayings they called out from one workbench to the next. For the time being, the only door in the shop that remained locked to him was his grandfather's office.

This loved the lumber shed even more than the workshop, at least when his grandfather was selecting wood. If he was there alone, the great structure with its open front and the light falling through cracks in the walls onto the piles of lumber was eerie. The layer of sawdust covering the floor was so thick it felt like walking on cotton wool as he followed his grandfather in his silent inspection of the stacks of lumber. He ran his large, hairy hands over a board here, sniffed another one there, until he found just what he was looking for.

His grandfather was a taciturn man with no desire to talk about school or discuss what This would do later, when he was grown up. He showed no interest in his report card, only in This himself. "You don't have to become anything, but you should do something!" That was his opinion. Although he loved his craft, he made no attempt to persuade This to be a cabinetmaker. Was his Grandfather a good at what he did? His dressers, chests, and tables were well-made and reliable, but nothing more. His chairs, on the other hand, were widely praised for their artless elegance. They were solid yet light as a feather. They floated. Everyone who lifted one of his chairs was astonished at how much it weighed, amazed that it had any weight at all. And then, chairs were one of the few things you could get his grandfather to talk about. "Tables? Anyone can make a table! But only people who know what they're doing can make a chair you can really sit on and anyone can afford! Sitting used to be a privilege. The master sat while the servant stood. Today it's different. Today, the chair does the standing for the lowly and weary as well as for the high and mighty. And an old man sitting down sees a lot more than a young man standing up!"

But most of the time, he was silent and This sat quietly on the tall stool his grandfather had made for him, watching the old man and the others as they worked, drowsy from the sound of their voices, the quiet music from the radio, and the noises of the machines and tools, content and enclosed in this cocoon of wood and sawdust.

He never went looking for happiness. It came and found him in the moments when he forgot about himself.

Chapter 3

He missed his wife, her voice, missed having her near. He wished he could tell her what he was experiencing, thinking, seeing in her absence. He took the cell phone from his pocket, placed it on the table, flipped it open, flipped it shut, nudged it back and forth, and finally stuck it back in his pocket, only to pull it out again, flip it open, and punch in their number before he had time to ask himself if he should call her or not. Daniela often took his calls as an attempt to check up on her or pressure her. They robbed her of the space she asked for and needed. Should he hang up? But she would see that he'd called in any case.

"Studers' residence."

Sometimes Anna forgot her snotty, insulted tone and sounded as open and carefree as she had been two years ago. In his mind's eye he could see her narrow, dark face and the way she always cocked her head and grabbed a strand of dyed-red hair with her right hand to twirl between thumb and forefinger as she talked to him.

"Anna! What's up? Everything OK? What're you doing at the moment?"

"Talking to you on the phone!"

"Anything else?"

"Not talking to you on the phone!"

He didn't give her the satisfaction of reacting. He just waited. He wanted her to sense that wasn't the kind of conversation he wanted to have. He heard her agitated breathing, then she cleared her throat.

"Can I ask you something, Pa?"

When had she last called him Pa? The name made his heart skip a beat but worried him at the same time. Why did he always have to lay every word she said on the scales, take every gesture she made as a reference, a sign?

"Of course you can, Anna. What do you want to know?"

"You think Baschi's weird?"

"Why? Did he do someth . . . "

"Just tell me," she interrupted. "Do you think he's weird or not?"

"He's your boyfriend, Anna, not mine."

"So you do think he's weird!"

"I didn't say that!"

"You must want to talk to Daniela."

"Anna! What'd Baschi . . ."

"She's not here!"

"You wanted to ask me something, Anna!"

"I did!"

"No, I don't think Sebastian is weird!"

"She's not here!"

"Maybe I don't understand him, but weird . . .?"

"Not in her studio, either," she interrupted.

"Anna!"

"But you can call her cell phone!"

"You know very well she doesn't have a cell phone!"

"Oh yeah, I completely forgot that!"

"Anna!"

"Gotta go."

"Anna! Let's . . ."

"Ciao!"

She hung up before he could answer. This threw the phone onto the bed and stepped out onto the terrace of the guest room. He knew Anna would regret her defiance and intransigence but wouldn't call back because that would be to admit she had acted badly. How much time and energy had he wasted in puberty rebelling against his parents' rules and ideas? And when had he finally understood that even the supposed self-chosen life is influenced by the rules and ideas of others and that he could deal with that? A handful of birds rose against the sky, a loose chain fluttering for a few seconds at the chimney of a house like a dark pennant, then dispersing in all directions.

Actually, it's no surprise that with each passing day he becomes softer and more even-tempered. Sometimes, he thinks someone could just blow on him and he would fall over with a grateful, magnanimous smile.

Daniela was forever losing things—keys, shopping lists, earrings, lipsticks, umbrellas, ID cards, addresses. For more than a week, she'd searched frantically for their mailbox key, then he found it one evening stuck fast to a box of pizza he was taking out of the freezer. For her forty-fifth birthday, he'd given her a cell phone she promptly left on the train. His wife had a touch of the absent-minded professor, constantly misplacing things, looking for her reading glasses when they were perched on her nose, capable of turning her wrist to look at her watch even though that hand was holding a cup of tea. This loved her, too, for the face she made as the hot tea poured down her legs and it didn't occur to her to turn the cup right side up again. One morning she walked into the kitchen with a dirty dust cloth in one hand and an empty yoghurt cup in the other. This and Anna looked on in astonishment as she dropped the dust cloth into the garbage can and tossed the yoghurt cup into the laundry basket . . .

The leather ball was underinflated, but that made it easier to head or stop with your chest. The best player was a small, quick black guy with a shaven skull that gleamed in the sun like a polished nut. Two others were wearing shirts and ties and playing barefoot in their boxer shorts. Henk had told This they worked in an office around the corner and played soccer almost every midday in the Vondel Park. The lawn was wet and made the ball fast. The other guys' passes, smartly kicked but not very precise, sent them running halfway across the field. In less than a quarter hour, they were so exhausted that they just stood in front of the piles of clothes marking their goal and waited for the offense to come at them. Then they left the game as they had joined it, with gestures that made words superfluous.

They walked a ways through the park and then sat down close to the water on an unmowed meadow in full sunlight that had already dried off the dew. Henk withdrew an embroidered sack from a shoulder bag that reminded This of the one he had had as a teenager. Henk took a lump of hash and a pipe out of the sack.

"Want some too?"

This nodded. The smell of the heated dope Henk crumbled into his cupped hand and mixed with tobacco filled This with an eager anticipation that surprised him. The windows of the expensive houses on the far shore had no curtains. He could see bookcases, oil paintings, leather chairs. A woman stood at one of the windows, holding a vase in her hand and contemplating the sky.

"You first."

This took the pipe and got a light from Henk. The smoke was so bitter he couldn't help coughing. So he laid back his head and barked as he had in his teens. The smell took him back: to see without being seen, cross the line out into a world where everything was a little different— displaced, drawn-out, softer, less urgent.

"Life is what happens while you're busy making other plans," said Henk, took two deep drags, and fell back into the grass.

"Says who?"

"John Lennon. Happiness happens to me the way life

happened to him. No sooner am I happy than I'm already thinking it'll pass and when it's over, I'll remember this happy moment."

"You're really fucking complicated," said This and took the pipe.

"No, I'm just pretty good at complicating things. Personally, I'm not complicated at all. So I remember how happy I was and how I was already thinking the happiness would pass."

"That's part of it."

"Part of what?"

"Being happy. Knowing that it will pass is part of the happiness. The secret of a happy life is not to give a shit about happiness, Henk!"

"I love life much too much to just want to be happy, anyway. Even happiness gets boring after a while. There was a guy in England a few years ago who celebrated Christmas every day. Every day he put three wrapped presents under a decorated tree and every day he ate turkey. Guess where he ended up."

"In the loony bin."

"Exactly!"

Henk took the pipe and sat up to take a deep drag.

"What do you think they hate most about us?"

"Who?" asked This.

"Women, stupid!"

"That we chew our nails."

"Fingernails or toenails?"

"Both!"

"Beer bellies."

"Hairy backs."

"Hairy toes."

"Bald heads. Feel anything yet?"

"Damn right I do! Halitosis! Women hate bad breath."

"So do we!"

"They can't stand hobbies either."

"You have a hobby?"

"Don't you?"

"That we can't dance."

"That we dance better than they do. Marjoke thinks my feet are ugly."

"Daniela loves my feet. But she thinks I'm not muscular enough."

"Muscles? Muscles are stupid."

"Muscles are for the ladies."

"Exactly!"

"Feel anything yet?"

"Don't you?"

Henk took a bottle of Evian from his bag and handed it to This.

"Here. Have a swallow."

The water was so cold it made his teeth ache. Each thing he saw was immediately shouldered aside by some new, seemingly even more important impression. It made him nervous.

"I think I'm going to be sick."

"You're already sick, This! Sick to death!"

"Think so? I'm not feeling anything."

"Not yet? Just wait!"

The lazy clouds overhead begged to be described, compared, and evaluated. The two friends lay next to each other and told what they saw. They blabbered and giggled. The grass was soft and took on the imprint of their bodies. Why were they sinking deeper into the earth with every drag? Weren't they light, lighter than air? They lay there laughing, talking, passing the time. Wind rustled the trees. There was a smell of cotton candy. The day lay before them, white and empty as a page waiting for the first entry. So thoroughly did the light wash out all color that it felt artificial. The air above the rooftops shimmered and the sky beyond led into outer space, where everything disappears into the void. Henk's laugh gurgled. In a flattened arc, an airplane followed the curvature of the earth. When This looked up again, its condensation trail had dispersed. It was very still. Leaves floated by on the murky water.

"I don't feel a thing," said This again. "Absolutely nothing."

Is the word friendship adequate to describe how close they felt?

They had eaten onion soup in a French bistro behind the Concertgebouw and now Henk wanted him to meet a bookseller in the neighborhood who specialized in jazz books and CDs. This was so tired he would gladly have lain down in one of the shady building entrances they passed. His legs were heavy as lead and he had a headache.

"Be right back," said Henk and disappeared into a shop whose little display window was empty except for a tobacco pipe and a match the size of a ski pole.

This walked on a few steps and dropped onto the bench of a streetcar stop. They had laughed so much his jaw hurt. The rails receding down the street shimmered in the evening light and seemed to merge into a thread of glowing iron. Through an archway he could see into the Vondel Park. The trees already lay in shadow and looked like churning green water that an invisible force kept from flooding the neighborhood. This stood up and started toward Henk who was lighting a cigarette in front of the shop. At that moment, a man emerged from the shelter of the trees and came toward them through the arch. He was carrying a tattered rucksack, filled to bursting, and took a few steps toward

This. Then he stopped, turned, and whistled through his fingers. Instantaneously, a dog shot out of the park, brindled white and brown, its left eye hidden in a spot. Since it ran with its body at an angle, as if in two directions at once, This was unable to see if it had a wound on its chest. Was it really the same dog that had frightened him two nights ago? At a second whistle from the man, the animal froze in mid-run and lay down, panting fast so that its sides rose and fell. Only now did This realize that the man was a homeless bum. He wore no shoes. His suit was filthy and tattered. He walked back toward the dog, which flattened itself against the asphalt, whining and looking anxiously up at its master. This felt a weight settle on his chest. Suddenly, he had to fight back the tears in his eyes.

Chapter 4

He resolved to make a detour around Züst's farm, but the next day he finds himself standing in the shadow of the barn again. The window above the trellis is open. The farmer and his hands are out in the fields and the barnyard is like a ghost town in the sweltering heat. This hears the tractor motor and the clatter of the hay rake.

What was the dog waiting for? Maybe for him? Why is it so hard to return its gaze? If This doesn't look away, then he becomes a participant in the animal's silence. They will be partners. The dog seems smaller than he did yesterday, more placid, and This considers going up to pet him, but the ripple that passes through the heavy body—a spring coiled and ready to jump forward—holds him back. Will the dog attack if he gets too close? Wasn't it sitting on the old army blanket next to the dog house yesterday? This notices for the first time that the chain runs across a pulley up under the roof. So the dog can move not just in a half-circle in front of the barn. He can also race up and down a long, invisible corridor, like a wolf in a cage.

This takes a step back. The sun has been warming his bare legs all afternoon. Now he feels them getting gooseflesh. The dog's gaze won't let him go, so he isn't aware of Züst's tractor until it drives into the barnyard. In a second, the dog is transformed into a different animal. It pulls in its head, lowers its eyes, a subservient hypocrite. The monster that has terrified This is itself terrified. He can feel his own fear disappearing, being replaced by disappointment and contempt. The farmer turns off the rattling engine, nods to This and disappears into the house, paying no attention to his dog.

It doesn't take long for the dog to make sure he's really alone again with the boy he has intimidated. And he realizes that the boy no longer fears him. This again sees the hate in his yellow eyes. Does he have an enemy now? Why? Because he was a witness to the dog's humbling by its master? The animal snarls and begins to growl, but stops immediately as Züst approaches them across the yard. With both hands, he carries a bag that drips blood. The sight and smell of the chunks of meat bulging against the white plastic drive the dog into an ecstasy of joy. He rises up on his hind legs, yelps, drops back onto all fours, and falls silent. His tail lashes the gravel. It looks like he's wagging his entire rear end. This cannot suppress a surge of joy at the animal's dumb happiness. The farmer gives This a self-important look; he's going to demonstrate something, give him a lesson. Züst says he must be interested in dogs and This nods vaguely. Züst takes a piece of meat from the bag, holds it humiliatingly close to his dog's snout, and says the animal's name is Rex. He's four years old and trained as an attack dog. Rex doesn't stir. Only his eyes leap back and forth between his master and the meat. A shiny thread of drool trails from his mouth. "Stay," says Züst in a gentle voice, "stay, Rex! See, that's what you call a good dog. Good boy, Rex." He waves the piece of meat in front of the animal's nose, which doesn't follow it but starts to tremble. The dog begins to give off an unpleasant odor that tickles This's nostrils. He's smelled it in the halls at school: the smell of absolute obedience. "OK, Rex!" Züst commands and lets the piece of meat fall. For years to come, This wondered how he could have missed the second when the hunk of meat disappeared into the dog's mouth.

"You see, that's what you call a good dog," says the farmer again, scratches the dog's head, and takes the next piece from the bag.

Isn't happiness related to fury and despair?

Chapter 5

He steps to one side as if to put some distance between himself and the others. We've seen this in people who feel uncomfortable appearing in public. He steps out of the spotlight's cone into the twilight at the back of the stage and raises the trumpet to his lips. Then he shakes his head and lowers it again, as if something has occurred to him, some annoyance. Just as it seems he wants to withdraw even further, something passes through his torso, no more than a ripple, a wave that must have originated in Henk's solo. After another moment's hesitation, he picks up the tune, quietly, using it as a basis for his own notes, overlaying it at first with soft restraint, then entering his own solo with total power and conviction. *Baby won't you please come home.* He hasn't always loved this tune. He doesn't like having to let himself go right from the beginning. He needs a warm-up, needs to sense that the other musicians are supporting him in case he falls, like a tightrope-walker's net.

Once he'd miscalculated the time. It must have been in the fall. In any case, it was already getting dark when he set out. The shadows were lengthening with every step he took and when he reached the trees, their trunks had grown together into an impenetrable wall. He walked along the edge for quite a while until his eyes grew accustomed to the dark and he dared to enter the forest. Where did all the sounds come from? It seemed forever until the garden gate appeared through the darkness as if painted with magic paint. Beyond the gate, the light from Grandfather's office cast a yellow quadrangle onto the grass. He saw the outline of the old man sitting at the window waiting for him, he pushed open the squeaking gate, took a deep breath, and ran to his grandfather as fast as he could through the gloom of the garden.

Today, he can even nail the high notes at the very end of the song. He lets them hang in the air like an incorporeal sculpture so beautiful no one dares move for fear of destroying it. It's frighteningly silent in the club. The moment of astonished tension lasts several seconds, an eternity, then a storm of ecstatic applause breaks out. It's as though people needed to get something off their chests: they scream, howl, whistle, cheer. He sees happy, sweaty faces, rolled-up sleeves, feverish eyes, couples hugging and kissing each other. Their music still seems to float in the *Kapitein Bird*. The floorboards of the stage are vibrating. Henk has the face of a boy sitting under a Christmas tree who's just unwrapped the one present he'd been longing for.

"Party afterwards," cries Henk across the stage. "We've been invited!"

"By who?" Willem wants to know.

"People with money. And a great cook."
"I'm not hungry, I'm thirsty! Thirsty!"

This followed Henk and Tim out the open door of the *Kapitein Bird* and into the spring evening. A man caught him by the arm. His face was red and his eyes shiny and he seemed lax and almost exhausted, as if something especially beautiful or especially terrible had happened to him. We can see that This doesn't recognize the man with the receding forehead and prominent, bulging brows. Could it be that someone who believes in humanity and fears nothing from it doesn't need to remember faces?

"Now, I don't care too much for jazz," said the man, "but that was . . . that was . . ."

He was much too keyed up to finish his sentence and gave a double thumbs-up instead.

"Don't you recognize me? The cosmetics salesman! From the train!"

"Did you hear us?" "It was great! Great! I'm speechless! And I thought I couldn't stand jazz! Can I buy you a drink?"

Henk turned around, looking for This. It had rained, the street behind him was dark, and if the sky had not been bright and almost inflamed, we wouldn't think we were in a big city.

"Come on, This!"

Henk hunched his shoulders, stuck out his ass, and walked down the street with his toes turned out. A few years ago, they had started doing impressions of how people walked after a concert. Months later, they'd quiz each other.

"Well?" called Henk over his shoulder.

"Barcelona. After our gig in the *Jamboree* three years ago."

"Wrong! But you can have another guess."

"Dornbirn. Year before last."

"Wrong! Come on This, you know this one!"

"Last year in Zurich. We were playing in *Moods*."

"Bingo!" shouted Henk. "And what kind of coat was his wife wearing?"

"She wasn't wearing any coat, because the guy was by himself!"

This took the sweating salesman by the arm and quickly pulled him past Henk. Only now did he notice that the windows of the *Kapitein Bird* were fogged up.

"Come on," This said to the man, "I'm inviting you."

After a few steps, he looked over his shoulder and saw Henk imitating the salesman's waddle. He'd lowered his chin and his forehead ploughed through the evening air like the bow of a ship through the waves.

Chapter 6

The attached houses on the Herengracht were narrow as dishtowels, but the people giving the party occupied three of them side by side, so theirs was generously proportioned. The lighted windows of the houses across the canal danced like lanterns on the tar-colored surface of the water, flowing together and breaking apart again. If you stand in one of these windows, thought This, it's like being on display. An excursion boat floated weightlessly by and disappeared as if he'd only imagined it. For a while, happy voices and dance music could be heard, then it grew quiet again on the water.

The room where the party was held was long and so cleverly lit that the few pieces of modern furniture blended into the background and seemed to float just above the parquet floor which creaked under every step. The guests at the other end of the room, bathed in an unearthly light that was nevertheless bright as day, looked like actors on a stage awaiting the director's instructions. The salesman was sitting on a leather couch next to a much taller woman who bent down to him as if examining his scalp. Diminutive Asian women in lime-colored, ankle-length silk dresses were serving champagne, wine, juices, oysters, and canapés, and since This couldn't keep all of them in view at the same time, he couldn't tell if there were five, six, or seven of the young women. He strolled along the wall, looking at the small, square, monochromatic paintings hanging there, and suddenly was brought up short by his own reflection in a big flat-screen TV. He saw that the door to his left, leading into the hallway, was vibrating in its hinges and at the same moment, he heard an airplane above the house, a howl that quickly faded away. Henk stood in the midst of a group of people blocking the hall and This stepped through a sliding door into a room where a floor lamp cast a pleasant light. Cut flowers stood in several vases on the parquet and filled the room with a perfume he felt as a stabbing pain in his forehead. In one corner of the room a woman sat on a leather hassock holding a glass of red wine smeared with her fingerprints. She looked at him. She was fifty or so, with a lively, open face despite the hardness at the corners of her mouth. She was wearing a gray pants suit made of iridescent material that rustled when she leaned forward to refill her glass from the half-empty bottle on the floor next to her.

"*De bloemen zijn von mijn man.*"

"They're very beautiful."

"*Ik vind dat ze stinken!*"

"You think they stink?"

She squinted, smiled, shook her head, and took such a deep breath that her nostrils quivered.

"*Maar ik hou toch van hem,*" she said, crossing her arms.

"Sorry, I don't speak Dutch."

"OK, let's talk German."

"What was that you just said?"

"That I love my husband anyway. Are you one of the musicians?"

This nodded. Her teeth were smeared with lipstick. Deeply-tanned skin stretched tightly across her collarbones and reminded him of leather. The woman was older than he had thought at first.

"My husband loves jazz!"

"What about you?"

"Me? I do too, but he's really crazy about it."

"Really crazy," said This, feeling like a total square.

"Oh, you Germans! You're such know-it-alls."

"I'm Swiss."

"Even worse," she said rudely.

The voices in the hall were raised. He heard Henk's laughter; when he'd had something to drink it always sounded like a whinny.

"You're a really good trumpet player," the woman said gently.

"You were there in *Kapitein Bird*?"

"I left before the end. Do you like photographs?" she asked, pointing to some pictures on the wall.

"As long as they're not of me."

Her sandals lay on their sides on the floor and the woman fished for their straps with her toes. She slipped into them and stood up a little too abruptly. She'd had enough to drink.

"In this one I'm seven!"

In the photo, a girl and a boy sat on a sofa beside a Christmas tree, unwrapping presents. The girl was brushing a lock of hair from her forehead and there was a look of fear in her eyes, fear she might miss something, fear the presents had been mixed up, fear the boy's present would be better.

"What do you think? Did I get what I wanted?"

This gestured vaguely, but the woman was absorbed in looking at the photo, not interested in his answer. The boy was peeling the wrapping paper from a fire truck, about to pull it free and raise it in triumph.

"Do you get what you want?" asked the woman

"Yes, I'm a lucky dog!" he said ironically.

"I hated the dictionary my parents gave me!"

She hunched her shoulders as if she was cold, then emptied her glass and handed it to This.

"Look at this one here. I was eleven . . . *of twaalf?*"

The photo had a slightly brown tint and showed a girl against a brick wall, smiling and holding up an orange for the camera.

"My mother used to give me an orange to take to school every day. You know that feeling when you break the skin with your fingernail and start to peel it?"

She sniffed at her fingers and her expression became distant, transfigured.

"I used to hate that smell you get on your fingers. Now I long for it. *Kent U dat ook?* . . . Know what I mean?"

"It's like getting kisses and hugs from your aunts and uncles. I hated that as a child. Now I miss it."

She looked at him in surprise, then smiled. For a moment, he thought she might kiss him.

"You think I should have another glass?" she asked, taking a step back.

"I dunno."

"Well then, I'll have another little one!"

She bent down for the bottle, refilled the glass This was still holding, took it from him and handed him the bottle.

"In this one, I'm meeting Axel."

"Axel?"

"*Mijn man.*"

There were about twenty young people in a group photo, gathered around an old man with long hair who sat on a camp stool and smiled broadly into the camera.

"That's Cees, my dissertation father. Is that how you say it in German?"

"Yes," This lied, "that's right."

It took him a moment to recognize the woman in the photo. She had on a sleeveless minidress and stood barefoot next to the old man. Curiously enough, This had no desire to ask her which of the young men was the one she would marry later.

"And that's where you met each other?"

"On that afternoon, yes. We slept together that night for the first time."

His grandparents were the only other couple This knew of who had a photo of the time they had met. The framed enlargement hung above the sofa in their living room and he used to study it for hours. His grandmother's father— his great-grandfather—had moved from near St. Gallen to a suburb of Zurich as a young man and gone to work for the railroad, but he remained a farmer all his life. He raised prize-winning rabbits and made it a point to take part in community organizations with his family. So This's grandmother had to sing in the mixed chorus although even her father admitted she had no voice and couldn't carry a tune to save her life. But if she hadn't sung in the mixed chorus, she wouldn't have gone to the cantonal choral festival in Wald in the Zurich Oberland and wouldn't have met her husband. The photo was taken at the end of the festival and showed the mixed chorus together with the "Harmonie Turicum" in which there was a young trumpet player. The photo documented the fact that he only has eyes for the singer standing at the end of the front row, her high spirits evident in her posture as she boldly returns his gaze. Anyone looking at that photo could see that the two were meant for each other, yet it had always made This wonder what would have become of them and what kind of life would they have led if his grandfather hadn't spoken to his grandmother right after the photo was taken. Or if she hadn't accepted his invitation to a glass of Veltliner in the festival tent. And what or who would he himself have become? His grandparents' next picture together was their wedding photograph, a framed enlargement that hung above their bed.

The woman cleared her throat, took the wine bottle out of his hand, and put it on the floor.

"How does one become a trumpet player, actually?"

Chapter 7

Because I was the only one in my family who could get along with my grandfather!

The wife of the man giving the party considered this for a moment, then laid a reassuring hand on his arm.

"Tell me about it." She sat down on the edge of the hassock and patted the empty space beside her. "Then I'll tell you what my grandfather taught me."

So This sat down next to the woman and started talking:

He was twelve the first time his grandfather brought him into his office. The desk stood in a corner, its surface such a hopeless jumble that he must have been weeks behind in his paperwork. No, even at twelve, This could see at first glance that this was no office. Grandfather's phonograph, speakers, and the record collection in a filing cabinet gave away what the room was really for. On the walls hung posters from jazz concerts and photos of black trumpeters. The song of the buzz saw was just barely audible from the workshop next door. "I've got something to show you, This," said his grandfather. "I mean, I want you to listen to something." He pointed to the two deck chairs by the window and This stretched out on one of them and watched as his grandfather turned on the record player, took an LP from the filing cabinet, and put it on the turntable.

That's how This discovered jazz.

His grandfather was a patient if somewhat long-winded teacher. He proceeded in great detail, leaving almost no one of any importance out, as This would realize later on: Clarence Williams and His Bottomland Orchestra, Fletcher Henderson, Duke Ellington, Louis Armstrong, Benny Goodman, King Oliver and His Orchestra, Henry "Red" Allen, Roy Eldridge, Sidney Bechet, Charles Lavere & His Chicagoans, Coleman Hawkins, Artie Shaw, Fats Waller, Nat King Cole, Ben Webster, Dizzy Gillespie, Gene Krupa, Lester Young, Count Basie. It took weeks to listen their way through his collection and it took a long time for This to like the music. He loved lying next to his grandfather, each on his own deck chair and if the weather was cool, each wrapped in an old army blanket with a long-since thread-bare red Swiss cross on it. The city was at their feet, fading into the twilight song by song while one by one, the lights went on. He found the jazz his grandfather never tired of playing for him comical at best, amusing, but at least different than anything he'd ever heard before. The record that finally made him into a fan was still one of his all-time favorites: "Nuff Said" by the Ben Webster Quintet, recorded February 8, 1944. The tune—leisurely, laid-back, but sprightly—opened a door inside him, put him into restless high spirits and made him want to do something right away. But what? His fingers twitched. He felt so acutely aware of his own body it scared him but also filled him with an overwhelming joy—or rather, overwhelming anticipation. He was alive! His grandfather opened his eyes, turned his head, and smiled at him. "'You're a ballad man, This. That's good, very good!' my grandfather said," said This while he watched the host's wife pour the rest of the wine into her glass. Her canines flashed, giving her face a wild unpredictability that made her attractive. What he didn't tell her was that years later, he'd turned the tables and introduced his grandfather to modern jazz. At first, his grandfather had rejected musicians like Miles Davis, Art Pepper, Charlie Mariano, and Kenny Wheeler, but soon This discovered him listening to Archie Shepp's *Fire Music*, for instance, snapping his fingers enthusiastically and whistling along with Shepp's solos.

"So now you know how I got to be a trumpeter."

"No, now I know how you discovered jazz. But even so it was a good story."

"It's not a story, it's the truth. And what did your grandfather teach you?"

"First you still have to tell me how you became a trumpet player!"

"Through my grandfather, of course. He'd played trumpet himself in years gone by, before he got married and opened his cabinet-making shop. He played in the village band and in a jazz combo. I managed to coax my first notes from his old trumpet and he was my first and best teacher. Whatever I can do, I got from him. 'You don't have to clench a pencil in your fist and plough the paper with it; you can hold it lightly and just let it glide across the page. That's how to tease warm tones from that cold tin, too. It's the only way to do it!' With that sentence he led me to my own sound. And now you have to tell me what your grandfather taught you!"

"That we humans leave this world alone. And that we'd better get used to it while we're still alive."

She listened to the echo of her words as if someone else had said them.

"Get used to what?"

"To being alone," the woman answered, kissed his cheek, and left the room.

One of his friends, a poet, took This to his study one day and showed him his very first typewriter. He hasn't used the turquoise Olivetti Baby for years, but it sits on a shelf above his desk and he can stroke its black keys whenever he wants. Their feel reminds him of his beginnings as a writer. This's first trumpet, a used B-flat jazz trumpet made by the Austrian firm Lechner, had a silver-plated body. It was a present from his grandfather on his thirteenth birthday and it now stands on a shelf in his practice room. He polishes it regularly with a cloth he uses only for that purpose. Once a year he disassembles it, puts the parts into a pan full of hot, soapy water, and cleans them with a brush. Then he rinses them in cold water, lets them dry, greases the tuning slides, oils the valves, and carefully reassembles it. Sometimes he picks up his first trumpet, raises it to his lips, and even works the valves, but it's been a long time—a long, long time—since he's actually played it.

For the past four years, he's played a Chicago Custom Mark II, built by the Englishman Andy Taylor. It has a matt gold finish, a .470 inch bore, titanium valves, a 3c nickel silver mouthpiece, a 140 mm bell, and a lead pipe turned from a single piece of solid brass. This isn't particularly interested in things technical, but he can reel off the fine points of his trumpet by heart.

Many years later, after his wife's death, This's grandfather basically started living in his office in the woodshop. The three steps leading from the garden into the workshop were half rotten. The wood they were made of felt soapy and spongy, like the tumble-down gazebo at the far end of the garden. As with many men who survive their wives, his grandfather began to go downhill himself. Before long, the only things he would wear were old overalls, a faded bathrobe, and worn-out sneakers. He stopped shaving and grew a beard that gave his face a sharp, raffish dignity. The deck chair became his bed, a lair he hardly ever left. Now, he entered the house he'd lived in with his wife for over forty years only to cook himself a little something. In time, he even stopped doing that and ate nothing but the small, wormy, but surprisingly sweet apples he shook down from the stunted trees in the garden. From one visit to the next, he seemed to get thinner, more translucent—a shrinking, paper man disappearing into himself as if performing some parlor trick. On This's last visit, he felt like he was sitting across from a stooped, exhausted child. Only his grand-father's ears seemed to have become larger rather than smaller. Fleshy and red, they hugged the small head that otherwise resembled a tortoise skull.

Months earlier, This had realized that his grandfather didn't have long to live. One evening he found the office empty and through the window, he watched his grandfa-ther approaching the workshop, stopping every few steps to catch his breath. His progress was excruciatingly slow, with drooping shoulders and hanging head, and more than once he had to stop and set down the bag he was carrying. It contained apples, as This later discovered. He wanted to run outside, help his grandfather, but was unable to move because suddenly, he couldn't get enough air. And he knew that nothing would be as it had been: his grandfather would die. This waited for the old man to finally enter the office, gasping for breath. Then from sheer relief that his

Grandfather had once again managed to gather apples, cross the garden, and conquer the three steps to the workshop, This scolded him for not eating enough.

Shriveled apple cores stood side by side on the window sill, a long row of them with their seed chambers bitten open and the pointed seeds scattered on the floor. The brown, discolored remnants of their flesh bore the imprint of his grandfather's teeth. That was the image This was left with, the one that ever since was the first to recur when he thought of his dead grandfather: shriveled apple cores on the sill of a window that looked out onto an overgrown garden.

Chapter 8

For five days, he's able to resist. For five days, he avoids Züst's dog. Then summer vacation begins and suddenly he has time to kill, time he doesn't know what to do with.

Next afternoon, he squats in the swaying green light of the cornfield, overhead the husks with their flaxen tassels, enclosing the ears and rustling as they rub together when the wind sweeps through the field in broad strokes, like a giant comb. Only a few more days and it will all be harvested. So pale it's almost white, the gravel road winds along the ridgeline and disappears in the shimmering heat. The lengths of plastic sheeting on the field look like caterpillars with distended bellies. He feels iron claws on the back of his neck yet has no choice but to do what he must do: he crawls out of the corn, stands up, and crosses the mowed meadow in the direction of Züst's barnyard.

The dance the dog performs at the end of his chain as soon as he catches sight of This doesn't scare him any more. At first it amuses him, then it makes him furious. Who does this mutt think he is? Rearing up on its hind legs, dropping back down, yelping like crazy and gasping for the air that seems to tremble around it. The dog is stupid. The time has come to punish it. But for what? For its humble obedience? Because it submits to Züst but not to him? Because a bag of bloody soup bones is all it needs to be happy? For its yelping rage? Does This even need a reason to punish the beast? Isn't wanting to enough?

The sun slants between the house and the shed, the shadows of the roofs loom toward him, soon he's standing in darkness. Why isn't he at the swimming pool with the other boys? There's saliva in his throat. If he could, he would simply turn around and leave. But the dog just won't calm down. Does an animal understand when a human is crying? He feels a knot loosen in his chest. He wants this moment to go on forever, this moment before he does it, but he knows that won't happen. Is he a grown-up now, now in this moment? The dog races up and down the corridor whose invisible walls are defined by the chain rattling over its pulley up under the roof. The farmer's out in the fields. In the fourth week of vacation, This is going to the shore with his parents, to Rimini. There's plenty of time until then.

Time for punishment. Time to see a new side of himself. Time to cast the first stone.

Chapter 9

The breakfast table of blond wood stood in a bay window and felt afloat in the swaying treetops. Marjoke had opened all the windows. They could hear the shrieks of a school class playing ball on a field in the Vondel Park, the chirping of birds, and the sound of distant traffic.

Henk put on some Dave Brubeck—side three of the

double album *The Great Concerts*. This knew what was coming right after the sax solo in the second cut, "The Real Ambassador." It had been recorded in the Conertgebouw in December 1963 and Henk claimed to have been there, even though he was barely five years old. In his solo, Paul Desmond played with phrases from "Pretty Baby," which This had never liked. It made him think of crochet doilies, spotless sitting rooms, and afternoon coffee and cake.

"There! Did you hear it? There, that first whistle—that's my father! And I was sitting next to him!"

"*In 1963 was jij vijf!*" said Marjoke and shot This a sly look with one raised eyebrow.

"What?" asked This.

"He was five in 1963," said Marjoke.

"So what? My father just . . ."

". . . knew the right thing to do. I know!" she interrupted him.

How many times had This heard this dialogue before? And how many times had he himself given Henk his cues? He knew which sentence would come next.

"You're all just jealous," he said a beat before Henk, as if one of them had muffed an entrance.

"Work on it a bit and you two can take it on the road!" joked Marjoke and turned off the record player.

Henk started to protest but she spread out the fingers of both hands and affectionately mussed his hair with them.

"Have you seen his new shoes yet?" she asked.

Henk waved one hand in deprecation but held up his right foot with the other to show This a canary-yellow sneaker.

"Those look like they must be your favorite shoes," said This.

"Do men have favorite shoes?" Marjoke asked.

"Not me!" said Henk.

"I do!" said This.

"Oh yeah?"

"High-top Campers that look like boxing shoes. Daniela bought them for me four years ago, in Rome."

"Butt ugly, they are!" Henk said solemnly.

"My first favorite pair of shoes were fire-engine red. There's a photo of me wearing them. I'm standing by my crib with a yellow sheriff's badge on my sweater and a toy revolver in my hand. Fire-engine red! I even wore them to school!"

"Boys don't have favorite shoes," said Henk.

"When I was seventeen, I had some moccasins I traded two Blood Sweat and Tears albums for at a flea market. Dark brown. I had to have them because Dickie Betts, the guitar player with the Allman Brothers, wore the exact same ones on the cover of *Brothers and Sisters*. Those were my second favorite shoes!"

"Men don't have favorite shoes," Henk stubbornly persisted.

"My first favorite shoes were black patent leather!" said Marjoke.

"Her favorites today are house slippers."

"You blabbermouth!"

"With tassels on them! Awful!"

"I wore those moccasins until they fell off my feet. Which they did at a campground in Stockholm. After that, I had low-top sneakers. Black and white, like Tom Petty."

"Converse," said Henk. "I had some too."

"He still does!" said Marjoke.

Suddenly the bay window was filled with amber sunlight. They fell silent, closed their eyes, and sat there as if at the bottom of a whiskey bottle, expecting a voice to speak and say what lay ahead. What would life bring? Life that would modestly start clicking past again as soon as a cloud intervened to extinguish the amber light.

On the Koningsplein, This followed Henk out of the streetcar and into a sporting goods store in the pedestrian zone. It reminded him of an art gallery or maybe a cell phone store. Sneakers and running shoes stood in glass cases that were open in front and back-lit in various pastel colors. The music—soft bass lines and ethereal synthesizer arcs—created a drowsy, subaqueous mood and conjured blissed-out smiles onto the faces of the sales people, who took no notice of them until Henk started pulling shoes out of the glass cases and putting them on the floor in front of This.

"*Mijn vriend heeft een andere manier van lopen nodig*," he said to a clerk wearing a soccer shirt and silver sneakers. "My friend needs something new to walk in—sort of like mine."

He pointed to his yellow Pumas and pushed aside the pairs that lay before This.

"He needs these exact shoes! In red!"

The shoes were incredibly light and fit like a second skin. This ambled up and down in the store like an actor getting used to the walk of a new character who's still a stranger to him. They were already at the cash register when This recalled one of his daughter's childhood drawings, a drawing of herself on a swing at the apex of its travel, so high up she was almost flying. On her feet she had drawn canary-yellow shoes so big they could have been wings. When he asked her what kind of funny shoes she was wearing she just looked at him and shook her head. "My flying shoes, of course!"

"Have you got the yellow ones in women's size 6 as well?" he asked the salesman.

"Does your wife have baby feet?"

"They're not for Daniela."

"They're for your girlfriend!"

"I haven't got a girlfriend any more than you do, Henk. They're for my Anna."

As they left the shop shortly thereafter, even here in tolerant Amsterdam people turned to look after them: two fifty-year-old men walking arm-in-arm through the pedestrian zone, obviously having the time of their lives and wearing yellow and red shoes. Despite their age.

How the two friends met may or may not be significant; we're going to tell it anyway. The stewardesses have already gone down the aisle closing the luggage compartments over the heads of the passengers in the flight from Amsterdam to Boston. This is just starting to think he really has once more been lucky enough to have an empty seat next to him. He's sitting on the aisle and the businessman in the window seat doesn't look like he wants to talk to an unshaven man in a denim shirt unbuttoned to reveal the collection of chains big and small around his neck. This slips off his shoes—a pair of sand-colored buckskin boots—and is about to spread out when a man storms in past the steward who is about to close the door. The belated passenger has long hair tightly gathered in a bun that hangs like a ball from the back of his head. He's wearing blue and white striped bib overalls, ragged sneakers, and a shirt of so many colors it looks like a child has painted it. As soon as This catches sight of this man, he knows he will sit down next to him. He's tall, broad, smells of garlic and hashish, and starts talking to This even before he's squeezed past him. We don't have to get into what they said to each other on the long flight. What's important is that they didn't stop talking even during the meal, that Henk spilled a glass of red wine onto This's white jeans, that they were both registered for a jazz theory course at the Berklee College of Music, and that they sensed—no, they knew—that a special friendship had begun, a friendship that had now lasted for twenty-two years.

Chapter 10

They work the strings that control the audience; they are the strings. Their playing is the ring in the bull's nose that makes him docile and tractable. They lay floors, construct walls made of air, spiral stairs leading nowhere, gloomy coal cellars, temples of glass, deserts.

He's going to remember this gig. There have been performances he'd rather forget or has already forgotten, but this one is the kind every musician dreams of. *It* plays with *them*. *They're being played*. They have to take care not to start playing too fast, must rein themselves in, put on the brakes. The face of Willem the bassist has a new angularity. The look on it could frighten us if we didn't know where it comes from: Willem has forgotten—no, lost track of—himself. And it's liberating, not disturbing. The tones of his bass begin in his body; he has become the instrument, setting up an oscillation in the room, a warm vibration that settles in the pit of your stomach. A high like this needs witnesses and they have them, more than a hundred of them. This is a good place to be, thinks This, and it's our doing. Our jazz turns this cellar into a sun-drenched plain, a mountain peak. It lays down a track, a trace. Let's see where it leads.

In the past, he's always thought Wayne Shorter's "Pinocchio" was too much of a tangle. He's never particularly enjoyed playing it, of course partly because he's familiar with Miles Davis's 1967 version and has always known he'd never ever be able to play a take like that—until today, that is. But today, he discovers what the tune conceals: the energy, the readiness to turn the world inside-out, take oneself by the hand and just set off. Where to? Into the open. Beyond himself. Is he really wearing red shoes? So what if he is? They fit like gloves, make each step as smooth as when he wore his moccasins. I'm not walking, he thinks, I'm flying. We're flying. And just now, in the middle of "Pinocchio," the most difficult piece in the whole set for the trumpet and saxophone, This and Arnold find each other. Up to now, their horns have clashed together like the antlers of stags in rut. Now they stand harmoniously side by side. Krabendonk the drummer is playing with such effortless power that This feels like setting down his instrument to listen, but he knows if he withdraws the tones of his trumpet from the airy filigree of their playing, it would collapse like a building being demolished, a monument that has lost its meaning. The audience is just as high as they are. Henk's face looks like he's just been told some incredible story. He catches his upper lip in his lower teeth as if trying to eat his own mouth. They try to take a break, but the audience, impatient to continue, calls them back from the dressing room and they keep on playing.

His grandfather's long, pale fingers were like marble and seemed suddenly so fragile he couldn't help looking furtively at them. With those fingers he had made his beautiful chairs, caressed his wife, and played his trumpet. They had been full of passion, full of power and devotion. Now they seemed worn out and translucent, apparently devoid of energy. But now and then, they would suddenly become animated. Twitching as if an electric current ran through them, they would begin to move to the rhythm of the music, supple, elegant, and precisely on the beat.

It was a long time before his grandfather screwed up the courage to fetch his old trumpet—his one and only trumpet—from the office closet and show it to This. As soon as the old man picked it up, his face softened and his eyes were transfigured. Over the years, the gilding had become matt, dull, and the bell had a little dent that gathered the light the way low ground collects water. First, his grandfather had explained the workings of the instrument in detail, naming each separate part, and This loved the words: mouthpiece tube, water key, finger ring, bell, tuning slide, brace. But he also sensed his grandfather using the words as an excuse not to play yet. In the end, however, he stood up, turned his back to his grandson, and put the trumpet to his lips. Did he not want This to see his face, his mouth, his lips? His tone was wobbly and hesitant, yet warm and surprisingly deep. The sound went right through This. How could a piece of cold tin sound so warm and full of feeling? His grandfather had flexed his knees a bit and finally, when his tone grew more confident, turned around and looked at This.

And the look in his grandfather's eyes had finally brought him to the point of wanting to play this instrument himself.

Chapter 11

Sometimes he slept at his grandparents' during school vacations. The little room with the guest bed was in the gabled attic and its window, not just framed but almost overgrown by ivy tendrils, looked out toward the vegetable garden. Lying in bed in the morning, he saw birds swoop in and disappear among the ivy leaves: sparrows, sometimes starlings, in twos, threes, fours, whole flocks of excited, noisy birds until the entire wall swarmed, raising a clamor that sounded like the creaking and sighing of a thousand rusty hinges. Usually he lay there for a while listening to the concert before he got up and stepped to the window, yawning sleepily. As soon as he did, a rustle of protest broke out and the birds scattered off in all directions. One morning in autumn—he must have been fourteen or fifteen—This happened to be present when the flaming leaves of the ornamental grape started to fall. He had just slammed the front door and was about to run over to the workshop when he noticed first one, then another let loose and twirl to the ground with soft finality, until at last whole bushels of them were falling, covering the courtyard in seconds with a red carpet.

The flock of sparrows that had transported him back to his childhood sat on the railing of Henk's terrace and rose into the air with a whirr and whoosh as he swung his legs out of bed. It was almost five-thirty. He'd slept only a few hours, but he had an uncontrollable urge to get moving and sniff the morning air. The sky was overcast, the light pale and hazy. Mist hung in the trees and condensed on the windows, veiling the view like a curtain. This got dressed and let himself out of the house.

Unpleasant weather takes the wind out of some people's sails. Daniela, for instance, gets depressed by fog and rain. She needs light and warmth. This Studer doesn't let the weather get to him. He draws confidence from the sun within. The wind is always at his back. The paths of the Vondel Park were deserted except for a few joggers and skaters. The lawns were covered with a milky sheen. The world looked like it wasn't all there yet. He fairly loped along. He would have breakfast in town, in a café on the canal at a little table with a view of the water. He'd write his wife the kitschiest postcard he could find, tell her how much he loved her and missed her. After a few minutes, rain suddenly began to fall in individual fat drops that left olive-sized spots on his t-shirt and transformed the pond into a sheet of beaten copper. It lasted barely two minutes, then it cleared up and the grass was flooded with sunlight. In the buildings all around, windows were flung open to give the interiors a breath of fresh air.

"Never, never put your trumpet away wet!"

Until finally, his grandfather forgot to keep breathing, forgot it like a habit grown so much a part of one's flesh and blood one gets bored and turns to some new activity that seems more important, more worthwhile. Death took him by surprise while he read. The open book on his lap was Gotthelf's *Uli the Hired Man* and on the turntable was Ben Webster's "No Fool, No Fun." Laburnum was blooming outside the workshop as if to fill the window with its heavy blossoms and close off for good the view out over the city.

We know our lives consist of thousands and thousands of decisions. We know too that it would have been a different life if, at one time or another, we had gone in a different direction. This Studer had intended to leave the Vondel Park near the Film Museum and head downtown along Museumstraat, past the Van Gogh and Stedelijk museums. But then he took the underpass instead, where it stunk of urine, and strolled through the narrow piece of park that reaches toward the Singelgracht. By now, leaden clouds edged in sulphurous yellow were rising beyond the buildings, obscuring the horizon. The light reminded him of the light in his wife's studio. He took the cell phone out of his pocket to share this moment with her and tell her he wanted to grow old—or older—together. But it occurred to him that the sentence "I want to grow old with you" might not really be such a compliment. Shouldn't you be doing everything in your power to live with the person you love instead of resigning yourselves to old age together?

This broke the connection before Daniela had a chance to pick up, put the phone back in his pocket, and felt a wave of weariness wash over him. What would have become of him if he had married someone else? What kind of person would Daniela be without him, what sort of woman without his love? And if he made her as happy as she made him, shouldn't he be able to take away her fear and distrust of life? A young street musician stood by the park gate playing the clarinet, slowing the steps of passers-by and making them break into smiles. This recalled catching sight of his daughter Anna not too long ago through the half-open door of his practice room. With surreptitious delight he watched her remove his trumpet from its case, raise it to her lips, and pretend to play while imitating his gestures and expressions. He had never been able to interest her in the trumpet. With his own daughter, he was a failure as a teacher; Anna had refused to learn any instrument at all. But a few months ago, through the closed door of her room, he'd heard her playing his old jazz records, much softer than she usually listened to music, but not through headphones, as if she wanted him to know.

Is the goal to stand empty-handed, waiting to catch and hold whatever's thrown to us? Is the goal to go from being empty-handed to holding something in your hands? Or is it the other way round? Happy he who can forget? Or heartbroken he who can't remember? He thinks about how other people call him a lucky dog and he has to agree. Yes, he's Sunday's child; confidence warms his hands, his chest, his brow. But happy-go-lucky he's not. Or is he? What's the difference between a lucky dog and a constant loser? Is it just in how they see the world? Doesn't happiness mean looking forward to the future?

As This Studer emerged from the park gate onto the sidewalk of the Stadhouderskade, he caught sight of the dog and the homeless bum who had startled him a few nights ago in the bushes opposite Henk's house. They were standing on the pedestrian bridge that crosses the gracht. The dog was trying to escape the reach of the bum. With his bulging rucksack over one shoulder, the man cursed as he yanked the animal toward him by the leash and raised his free hand to strike.

There's a kind of knowledge that stows away in our subconscious. We don't notice it because it's practiced at staying concealed as it travels along with us. A knowledge that must stay hidden because it would destroy us.

Then This stepped into the street to run to the dog's aid. His shadow stretched out across the asphalt, a man on his way to make good an old wrong, his shadow, the dark doppelganger with stilts for legs, sliced in two by the streetcar tracks.

Chapter 12

In the second week of summer vacation there was a change in the weather. Rain arrived that would last all summer, at least in his memory. He awoke to the drumming of drops against his window and fell asleep to the drumming of drops on the roof tiles. Brooks became rivers and rose over their banks. Pastures and fields soon turned into lakes. The blanket of clouds hanging over the land like a gray towel opened only to make way for more storm clouds. The world was saturated like a blotter full of ink. Their faces empty, people hurried through streets studded with deep puddles. Everyone who could afford to escaped to the south. Those who had to stay at home were sullen and testy. The vestibule of his grandfather's woodshop smelled of the workers' damp clothes. They got into each other's hair over every little thing. On some days, the rain carried foreign smells across the city—scents of distant continents that made people lift their noses and sniff the air as they did in childhood, impatient for the first snow.

This Studer had tormented Züst's dog for two weeks. He'd thrown stones at him—gravel at first, then real rocks with sharp edges. With a slat he found in the shed, he'd driven him into a corner and hit him. He never thought about what he did and why he was doing it. He was addicted to the whimpering and yowling, addicted to the fearful, pleading look of the dog. Had he not subjugated him? He had become the master and now he could walk up to him, magnanimously scratch his skull, and let him lick his hand.

On August 7, 1966, he does the dog the favor of taking a step toward him, just one step, but it's enough. The dog knew this moment would come. He's waited patiently, seething with hate. One step and he has the boy. This registers the change in the dog's eyes, but it's too late. The animal has already risen onto its hind legs, mouth quivering and haunch muscles tensed. This hears the rear paws scratching for a better foothold, then it's at his throat. He's just able to get his hand in front of his face and push its front paws down so he doesn't lose his right eye. The dog is so strong and full of hate it knocks him right onto his back and squats on him, lies on him, snapping and slavering, and sinks its teeth into the boy's chest.

Never again in his life will This get this close to a dog. This day has seen to that. Under other circumstances, could they have been friends? He, the neighbor boy who takes the farmer's dog for a walk, feeds it, teaches it tricks, shares his thoughts with it when no one else is listening?

How long is it before the dog's yellow eyes widen, its jaws loosen and let go? To This it seems an eternity. Didn't the sky change color? What would the dog have done to him if the farmer hadn't intervened? Züst was beside himself with fury and disappointed pride and struck at the beast again and again with a piece of plastic hosing.

This sees his reflection in the glasses of the doctor bending over him to sew up the bite wound on his chest and the deep gash under his eye.

Rex was put to sleep the same day This and his parents left for their vacation in Rimini.

Chapter 13

The number 2 streetcar came screeching to a stop. That's how mundanely our story ends.

And This Studer? The impact threw him a few meters to the side. He lay on his back on the pavement, wearing his new red shoes, his arms spread as though to embrace someone.

He felt nothing, no pain, not even fear of the end. Nor did he see the film we're always promised for this moment, the final film that's supposed to show us our entire life again with all its happiness, all its sadness. He stared at the receding sky, felt cold, raised his right hand toward his face and moved his fingers. We've gotten to know him a bit and can see he imagines that he's playing the trumpet, one last song—or perhaps the first in a long series of new songs he has yet to learn? He saw the sky, a washed-out screen crossed by a wavering stream of birds, and then the face of the conductor, bending over him in concern and taking his hand. What was the man saying? "Being happy always begins just a little above the earth," thought This. Where'd he get that from? And where was the dog? Disappeared. If we could rise into the air, up over the trees and the buildings like the end of a movie, we would see him racing through the Vondel Park in great leaps, farther and farther away, until finally he dives into the bushes and presses his trembling body against the earth.

And the bum? He quickly disappeared into the maze of streets around the Leidseplein. And life in general quickly resumed its course, whether or not a man was lying in the street. The world continued to turn; are we surprised? Old men bent over bathroom sinks as they always have. Bachelors longed for someone to think of them. Housewives stood at windows looking out onto suburban streets slick with rain. Children feared school yet sang happy songs as they trotted along in front of their grandparents. And somewhere someone was surely closing a curtain, turning on the radio, leaning back to listen to the music and peacefully smoke the first cigarette of the day.

Yes, life really did resume its course as if nothing had happened. Henk, for example, stood in the bay window of his living room and was overcome by a sudden dizziness that came from nowhere and cast a shadow over him. He put a hand on the back of a chair to steady himself, closed his eyes, and for the space of a heartbeat felt wonderfully light, as if a burden had been lifted from him. At the same moment, Anna lay next to Baschi on his parents' sofa and was seized by a wave of emotion so intense it frightened her. The shiver that passed across her bare arms soon spread over her whole body. She hugged Baschi with all her might and he looked at her in astonishment, gasping for breath. And Daniela? Daniela sat at her potter's wheel feeling tired and grumpy since she'd hardly slept a wink, when she suddenly realized she'd just made the most beautiful cup of her life, as if it had dropped into her lap in a fairy tale. A container made to contain nothingness. "This cup is for This!" she thought and turned toward the window. Sun streamed into the studio and a blurry flock of birds could be seen. "It's for my husband, to put next to the one that began our love."

But for This Studer, everything started to go too fast, much too fast. He was falling. He no longer had the strength to hold himself back. He fell. And let go. A glass doesn't break if it doesn't get broken—was that his last thought? What doesn't exist now never will. The well ordered city stood in the soft light of morning and couldn't have cared less. Most people are blind to the gift they've been given. They suffocate on their own breath, let their own weight drag them further and further down. Fortune is not blind. Blind are those who can't see it, don't want to see it. Weren't the new shoes a little silly after all for a man of his age? Now the sky had lost all color. This saw a stretch of ocean before him—open ocean, that blue promise—and gulls above it, sailing the wind. He didn't grasp right away that the image had frozen, come to a standstill. He had arrived. He let his arms sink and pulled his knees to his chest, a child.

Let him go. There's nothing more we can do for him.

TITLES IN THE COMPANION SERIES
THE ART OF THE NOVELLA

BARTLEBY THE SCRIVENER / HERMAN MELVILLE

THE LESSON OF THE MASTER / HENRY JAMES

MY LIFE / ANTON CHEKHOV

THE DEVIL / LEO TOLSTOY

THE TOUCHSTONE / EDITH WHARTON

THE HOUND OF THE BASKERVILLES / ARTHUR CONAN DOYLE

THE DEAD / JAMES JOYCE

FIRST LOVE / IVAN TURGENEV

A SIMPLE HEART / GUSTAVE FLAUBERT

THE MAN WHO WOULD BE KING / RUDYARD KIPLING

MICHAEL KOHLHAAS / HEINRICH VON KLEIST

THE BEACH OF FALESÁ / ROBERT LOUIS STEVENSON

THE HORLA / GUY DE MAUPASSANT

THE ETERNAL HUSBAND / FYODOR DOSTOEVSKY

THE MAN THAT CORRUPTED HADLEYBURG / MARK TWAIN

THE LIFTED VEIL / GEORGE ELIOT

THE GIRL WITH THE GOLDEN EYES / HONORÉ DE BALZAC

A SLEEP AND A FORGETTING / WILLIAM DEAN HOWELLS

BENITO CERENO / HERMAN MELVILLE

MATHILDA / MARY SHELLEY

STEMPENYU: A JEWISH ROMANCE / SHOLEM ALEICHEM

FREYA OF THE SEVEN ISLES / JOSEPH CONRAD

HOW THE TWO IVANS QUARRELLED / NIKOLAI GOGOL

MAY DAY / F. SCOTT FITZGERALD

RASSELAS, PRINCE ABYSSINIA / SAMUEL JOHNSON

THE DECEITFUL MARRIAGE / MIGUEL DE CERVANTES

THE LEMOINE AFFAIR / MARCEL PROUST

THE COXON FUND / HENRY JAMES

THE DEATH OF IVAN ILYICH / LEO TOLSTOY

TALES OF BELKIN / ALEXANDER PUSHKIN

OTHER TITLES IN
THE CONTEMPORARY ART OF THE NOVELLA SERIES

THE PATHSEEKER / IMRE KERTÉSZ
THE DEATH OF THE AUTHOR / GILBERT ADAIR
THE NORTH OF GOD / STEVE STERN
CUSTOMER SERVICE / BENOÎT DUTEURTRE
BONSAI / ALEJANDRO ZAMBRA
ILLUSION OF RETURN / SAMIR EL-YOUSSEF
CLOSE TO JEDENEW / KEVIN VENNEMANN
A HAPPY MAN / HANSJÖRG SCHERTENLEIB
SHOPLIFTING FROM AMERICAN APPAREL / TAO LIN
LUCINELLA / LORE SEGAL
SANDOKAN / NANNI BALESTRINI

THE CONTEMPORARY ART OF THE NOVELLA

Made in United States
Troutdale, OR
09/28/2023

13254329R10076

THE LITTLE BOOK
OF THE
ICELANDERS

ALDA SIGMUNDSDÓTTIR

THE LITTLE BOOK OF THE ICELANDERS

LITTLE BOOKS
PUBLISHING

TABLE OF CONTENTS

Introduction. 7

1   The independence thing. 13

2   Informal addresses. 18

3   Them Icelanders have some weird professions. . . . 21

4   Who are your people?. 23

5   Kindly leave your sentimentality at the door. 25

6   Going for it. 27

7   Patro, matro ... or both?. 30

8   As for family names 32

9   Nicking a name. 34

10 Passing names. 37

11 Applying names. 38

12 Traditions in names. 40

13 Name visitations 42

14 Turning a foreign name native. 43

15 Of optimism. 45

16 Things working out. 48

17 Work or cheat. 49

18 Being at the last minute. 50

19 The busy little country that could. 52

20 Curse of the canine cleaners. 54

21 Death by dog. 58

22 That bizarre email frustration. 60

23 The upside of not planning ahead. 62

24 Iceland, where traffic laws are guidelines. 64

25 That curious aversion to signage. 67

26 In Iceland, women are men. 69

27 Wery wery kind. Wery kind. 71

28 How about that narcissistic party behaviour?. 72

29 No apologies, we're Icelandic. 74

30 The invaluable social function of the hot tubs. . . . 75

31 Beware the wrath of the shower police. 77

32 Reykjavík nightloot. 79

33 And with that, we segue into the alcohol problem. . 83

34 Beer: the devil's mead. 84

35 On being *flott*. 86

36 Raising the complication level. 88

37 Invasion of the foot massagers. 90

38 House proud. 91

39 Of birthdays and big birthdays. 93

40 The ingenious quota system. 95

41 However, if you are overseas. 98

42 How do you like my insecurities?. 101

43 It's a family affair. 103

44 On convoluted family ties. 105

45 Embracing babies. 107

46 Snoozing in the open air. 109

47 On confirmation. Or should that be conformation. . 112

48 On graduation. 115

49 On marriage. 118

50 On dying. 120

About the author. 125

INTRODUCTION

Dissecting the psyche of a nation is a daunting task. It is also doomed to failure. It's absolutely impossible to make a claim about "the Icelanders" without someone popping up and saying, "Yes, but ... but ... but ... I'm not like that!"

"I don't drive like a bandit!" "I don't hate dogs!" "I don't invite 100 people to my birthday parties and pay for all the booze myself!" "I don't mix up my v's and w's!" "I know how to have conversations with people!"

All of which will be true. Which is why we need to get something out of the way right now: this book is stuffed with sweeping generalizations and subjective opinions, armchair philosophies and random musings. No special studies were carried out in the writing of this book. And when I refer to "the Icelanders" I do so completely generically – though I do like to think those statements will apply to at least a handful of Icelanders. Ideally the majority.

Plus, there's this: every time I think I've found something concrete to say about the Icelandic national character, I come up against a paradox. The need for independence vs. the need to be connected. Among the happiest people on earth vs. consuming the greatest amount of anti-depressants of all the Nordic

countries. Well-travelled and cosmopolitan vs. hopelessly provincial. Grasping the national psyche of the Icelandic people is like trying to catch a slippery fish with your bare hands.

I moved back to Iceland in 1994. At that time I'd just crawled out of my twenties and had lived abroad more or less since the age of five. I had a respectable command of Icelandic and no telling accent, an Icelandic name, and passed for a native in most respects. But make no mistake: I was a foreigner. Granted, I had "my people" here, but since I had not grown up with them, they were effectively strangers. And since I'd not been a part of the Icelandic school system (apart from three hazy years between the ages of seven and ten) I didn't belong to any groups or cliques or even sewing circles – those social constructs so ubiquitous among Icelandic women. This set me quite distinctly apart from most Icelanders, who tend to form those sorts of groups in elementary or secondary school and retain them more or less throughout their lives, for better or worse.

So because I had all the trappings of a normal Icelander, I was instantly regarded as "one of us". But having been socialized on a different continent, I was completely ignorant of the many social customs and standards that prevailed in Icelandic society. This garnered me some pretty strange looks and even hostile reactions in those early days. I can still remember sitting in the coffee room at work one day, less than a year after moving back and after my first Christmas holiday, when everyone was talking about what they had served for dinner on New Year's Eve. I said I'd cooked some *ýsa*, or halibut. The room went silent and suddenly all eyes

were on me. Some people even fidgeted, like I'd said something very awkward. I was perplexed. *What exactly did I say?*

What I did not know then was that Icelanders do not eat mundane food like ýsa on New Year's Eve. (Not even if they cook it in an extra-special way, like I did.) Both Christmas Eve and New Year's Eve are steeped in tradition in Iceland, and that tradition dictates – among other things – that people need to cook something extraordinary on those days. In fact, what people plan to eat on Christmas or New Year's Eve is a popular topic of conversation all through December, and beyond. It's the sort of thing you talk about at Christmas parties. When you run out of things like the weather.

In other words, tradition is of extreme importance to the Icelanders. So is conforming. Soon after moving back I rented a basement apartment from a lady who lived on the upper floor in the same house. She chose me from among several prospective tenants (rental properties were pretty hard to come by at the time – and still are) because, as she put it, "we just want to have people like us living here". It was put forth in a perfectly sweet and amiable manner, and describes rather well the prevailing sentiment in Icelandic society, where that which comes from outside is just a little bit uncomfortable. Alas, she found out to her dismay that I was not much like her at all and I think it upset her world view a little bit – at least until I moved out and she was able to rent the place out to someone who was more her type.

Incidentally, I don't think most Icelanders realize to what extent those unwritten rules and customs govern their lives – much in

the way fish don't know they're wet. Which I guess is normal, and understandable. There is a collective need among the Icelanders to stand together and not rock the boat – something that is largely unconscious and which served the nation well throughout the ages, when people's very survival depended on everyone doing just that. This togetherness also provides a sense of comfort and security that is reassuring in myriad ways. There is something inherently good in many of the prevailing traditions and cultural norms, like wrapping yourself in a warm, cosy blanket. But, like many other sources of comfort, there is a line you can cross, and when you do those things suddenly become self-defeating and even suffocating.

Most Icelanders realize this, and recognize the value of going abroad to live for a longer or shorter period. Indeed, the Icelandic word for "stupid" is *heimskur*, which is derived from the word *heima*, or "home". In Iceland, the person who is heimskur is the person who has not left home.

A few words about the structure of this book. There isn't one. When I sat down and decided to write it I basically just wrote down 50 things that I thought were kind of quirky about the Icelanders, and went from there. Afterward I thought I probably should have tried to group things in a more organized fashion, with special chapters focusing on different aspects, like "National Psyche" or "Quirks" or "Traditions" or whatever, but the thought of going back and reworking things to fit into that sort of model seemed to me kind of self-defeating, like it might kill all the spontaneity. (OK, maybe I was just lazy.) I've made a cursory nod

in that direction by at least trying to cluster things together, with limited results, I fear. Most of this stuff is pretty random. Also, advance apologies: I seem to have been a little bit obsessed with names and naming traditions … I have no idea why, but there are several blurbs with that sort of focus.

Incidentally, I should mention that this book was initially written for the readers of my now-abandoned blog, icelandweatherreport.com, who had come to be familiar with my sometimes warped humour and weird terminology. I tend to refer to Iceland as the Land of the Nice (or Niceland) – which may be sardonic, or genuine, depending on the context. I also use cuss words, though when I need to use the really bad ones I give you the printed version of the beep (*) 'cause I'm a laydee. Finally, you might occasionally find something resembling understatement or sarcasm or deadpan irony on these pages, which should be understood as either understatement or sarcasm or deadpan irony.

Also, this book that you now hold in your hands, read on your screen, or listen to on your device, is the second edition of *The Little Book of the Icelanders*. The first edition was initially published in 2010 and had, when eight years had passed from its publication, become somewhat dated. Most of the sections in this book are the same or similar to the original, but a few have been replaced or extensively updated to reflect social trends or changes.

On that note, and without further ado, I invite you to join me in probing the national psyche of the Icelanders.

1
THE INDEPENDENCE THING

The first thing you should realize about the Icelanders as a nation is that they value their independence above all else. This is not surprising. The Icelandic nation was oppressed for centuries, first under Norwegian, and then Danish, rule. As a colony, Iceland became desperately poor. Since its full independence in 1944, however, it has prospered. The fear of subjugation is deeply ingrained in the DNA of the Icelanders.

You may already know that the Icelanders are a literary bunch. They love books and are very proud of their literary heritage. And rightly so. The literature that was produced in Iceland in centuries past, including the Icelandic sagas, is considered one of the most valuable cultural contributions to world history. On this faraway hinterland in the northern seas,

on the edge of the inhabitable world, where food was scarce and the climate harsh and unforgiving, folks sat in their turf abodes and wrote lengthy histories and chronicles of the Nordic kings, settlement of nearby lands, pagan gods and beliefs, and much more, all on vellum, the production of which is a chapter unto itself. The Icelanders have no palaces or stunning monuments of which to boast, but they do have their manuscripts, which they count among their most valuable national treasures.

That pride in the literary heritage was in no way diminished when, in 1955, Icelandic author Halldór Laxness was awarded the Nobel Prize for literature. At the time, the population of Iceland was a mere 156,000 people, so making such a splash on the world stage was considered, well, pretty awesome. Mind you, Laxness had not been wildly popular in Iceland before that time – many folks took serious exception to his frank portrayal of the Icelanders as gruff ruffians living in turf huts, steeped in grovelling servitude to the Danish, among other things. But all was forgiven with the awarding of the Nobel Prize, and Halldór Laxness – who died in 1998 at the age of 96 – became a national hero. Today Laxness is widely thought to have captured the essence of the Icelandic soul better than anyone else in his work, not least in the novel *Independent People*, the story of the peasant farmer Bjartur í Sumarhúsum (Bjartur of Summerhouses) and his obstinate struggle for autonomy. Given the Icelanders' deeply rooted need for independence, Bjartur is often considered the quintessential Icelander.

This mad desire for independence manifests in innumerable ways. One of the most obvious is the profound dread some people have of joining the European Union, a debate that crops up every few years. The older generation – those old enough to remember Danish rule, or at least the collective sense of freedom when the shackles were finally cast off in 1944 – is especially opposed to EU membership. What makes their arguments particularly illogical, however, is that Iceland is already a member of the European Free Trade Association, or EFTA – a deal that was also vehemently opposed by a large portion of the population when it took effect in 1993. EFTA membership means that Iceland must abide by some 80 percent of the EU's laws and regulations, without having any say in the creation of those laws, or the option to vote in their favour. One could thus conversely argue that Iceland is even less free in relation to the EU than it would be as a full member.

Another manifestation of this hankering for independence is the Icelandic desire to own, rather than rent, property. The value of owning your own home is deeply entrenched in the mindset of the Icelandic people. The rental market has traditionally been very small in Iceland, and renting is almost always considered an interim solution – an evil necessity either before you are solvent enough to buy, or while in between home purchases. Owning your own property is considered synonymous with security.

I should state, though, that over the past few years it has become more and more difficult for Icelanders to purchase their

own homes – especially first-time buyers – as property prices have gone up drastically over the last decade or so. There are two main factors responsible for this. One, the sharp rise of property investment companies in the wake of the economic meltdown and subsequent capital controls, which forbade large-scale transfers of money out of Iceland. Since foreign investment became closed to Icelandic businesses, these investment companies sought out local ventures, and found them in real estate. Hundreds of apartments were bought up in Reykjavík's downtown area, and both rental and property prices soared. The other major factor pushing housing and property prices up is not only a problem in Iceland, but also in countries and cities around the world. I am speaking, of course, of Airbnb. With so many properties being used as lucrative short-term rentals for tourists, fewer are available for the locals, resulting in a shortage of housing and therefore higher prices.

Still, these seismic shifts on the housing market have not changed the Icelanders' eagerness for owning their own property, and it is still an important component in the Icelanders' view of themselves as independent people.

Yet another symptom is the Icelanders' propensity for always doing things at the last minute. (More on that later.) This apparent tardiness applies to everything from showing up at an appointment, to booking a summer holiday. I suspect,

however, that it has less to do with tardiness and more with an insidious fear of commitment that seems to plague many Icelanders ... which again harks back to the independence thing, because fear of commitment is really fear of restricting your independence. If you book a holiday that's supposed to happen nine months from now, you're compromising your freedom and independence, right? So better to wait until the last moment. After all, something better may come up.

And a Pandora's box that I am reluctant to open, but which has to be mentioned in this context, is the whole issue of whaling. Iceland still hunts whales, despite strong international pressure to stop. The response of Icelandic authorities has traditionally been that bowing down to that pressure would be a major restriction of Iceland's sovereignty as a nation. Indeed, the very day before I write these words in late 2018, an award dubbed the "Freedom Award" was presented to Hvalur hf., the sole company in Iceland engaged in commercial whaling. The accolade was handed to the company by the Young Independents, the youth wing of Iceland's dominant Independence Party, a political party that has been in power consecutively, with the exception of one four-year term, ever since Iceland obtained independence from Denmark in 1944. Hvalur hf. was given the award on the grounds that it continues to "fight for whaling in Icelandic waters". Evidently whaling, in the view of Icelandic authorities, is not an economic matter

(there is little demand for whale meat among the Icelandic population), nor a question of heritage, but a matter of maintaining the country's precious independence. Irrespective of how the rest of the world disagrees, irrespective of all the pressure from animal welfare groups, irrespective of the damage to Iceland's image and reputation, irrespective of the complete lack of logic in any of it, whaling does and will continue because dammit, no one is going to tell a sovereign, independent Iceland what to do!

2
INFORMAL ADDRESSES

Here's something you should probably be informed of early: the Icelanders address everyone by their first names, regardless of that person's age and social standing.

Children address adults by their first names, and adults address everyone, no matter what their position in society, by their first names. Including the president.

If you are a child and your teacher's name is Ljótur

Ormsson, you will call him Ljótur, not Mr Ormsson. Your friends' parents will be Jón and Gunna, as opposed to Mr and Ms whatever.

People are also listed by their first names in the phone directory. In the old days when the phone book was printed (they did away with the paper version in 2016), you would look under L and not under O when looking up Ljótur Ormsson. The modern online version of this, of course, is that you type in Ljótur, as opposed to Ormsson, in the search field.

The only thing sometimes used to differentiate a person of importance is to place *Herra* (Mr) or *Frú* (Mrs or Ms) in front of their names. Today this is reserved for the head of state or the bishop of the National Church – and even then, it is rare, and mostly reserved for formal correspondence and addresses.

Personally, I am a big fan of this informality. It frees you from invisible constraints, barriers and perceived class distinctions. It's direct and simple – a great asset in a complicated world.

3
THEM ICELANDERS HAVE SOME WEIRD PROFESSIONS

Speaking of the phone directory.

As I said, all people are listed alphabetically by their first names. Then comes their last name, their profession, and their home address.

Example: *Jón Jónsson, bóndi, Sólargeisla 77, 177 Reykjavík.*

You don't need any official proof of your profession to have it listed in the phone book. Meaning you don't need to show up with an official piece of paper that says you are, in fact, a lion tamer or trapeze artist.

You can finally unleash those childhood dreams – make your profession be whatever you want!

You see where this is going, right? Yup, the Icelandic phone directory lists people with some pretty, er, unconventional professions. Did you know, for instance, that in Iceland there are, at the time of writing, six *winners*, ten *sorcerers* (and one *ex-sorcerer*), three *alien tamers*, 11 *cowboys*, one *cowgirl*,

62 *princesses*, six *princes*, ten *kings*, 12 *queens*, five *drama queens*, 19 *ghost busters*, one *ex-Coca-Cola guzzler*, one *unicorn tamer and Jedi master*, and one *hen whisperer*?

A chapter unto themselves are the *not*-professions. These are often the product of people trying to differentiate themselves from someone well-known who has the same name, usually because they've been getting too many phone calls intended for their better-known namesake. Examples (yes, these are real ones): Ellen Kristjánsdóttir *not the singer*, Baldvin Ómar Guðmundsson *regular guy, not the goalkeeper*, and Magnús Lárusson *not the golfer*.

And then there are the random *nots* that have nothing to do with famous people: *not a boy scout*, *not a summer house owner*, *not green* (huh?), *not from Siglufjörður*, and my personal favourite, by a man whose first name is Örn (the Icelandic word for eagle) *not a bird*.

Ah, the Icelandic phone directory: an endless source of amusement.

4
WHO ARE YOUR PEOPLE?

Not so many years ago, when you as an Icelander went to meet the parents, or grandparents, of your new flame, you needed to be prepared for the question: Who are your people? (Icelandic: *Hverra manna ertu?*)

This meant, of course: Who are your parents, your grandparents, your ancestors? With such a small population it was easy for people armed with that information to position you in the grand Icelandic scheme of things, though occasionally consulting a genealogy book or two might have been required.

Nowadays, though, with the sum total of human knowledge in our pockets, we Icelanders have the luxury of logging on to a website called Íslendingabók (the Book of Icelanders – no relation to this *Little Book*) – an online genealogy database that will trace our lineage back hundreds of years with just a few clicks.

It is a fascinating resource. For example, several years ago I was translating a historical novel, that was based on true records, from Icelandic into English. By logging on to Íslendingabók I could see that I was related to one of the

main characters 14 generations back, and by clicking on all the names in between I could determine that "my people" had in fact been from the very same region in which the book was set. So cool.

Also, Íslendingabók informs me that I am directly descended from the first settler of Iceland, Ingólfur Arnarson, 29 generations back. But then again, so is almost every Icelander, give or take a generation or two, so that's not likely to earn me any street cred (boo).

But it is not all a bag of delights when it comes to the Íslendingabók site ... or, to be more precise, when it comes to the related phone app that was developed when everyone began using smartphones. Some wisecracking website caught a whiff of this novelty and decided to write a story about what they, in an exorbitant display of craftiness, dubbed Iceland's "incest app". According to them the app was a brand new invention designed to make sure that people who hooked up, say at a bar, did not go home with their cousin or other relative. Pretty salacious, you have to agree, and as we know the media loves a salacious story. The myth of Iceland's incest app was born, and it still lives a robust life on the intertubes. Any attempt to tell the truth – that the incest app is really an innocent genealogy app that grew out of a website that had been around for over a decade – has proven fruitless. Once you cut off one head of this beast of a story, two more seem to grow.

5
KINDLY LEAVE YOUR SENTIMENTALITY AT THE DOOR

It has to be said: one of the best things about the Icelanders is their humour.

The Icelandic sense of humour is dry, self-effacing, sardonic, and deadpan, with a special affinity for the absurd. Icelanders abhor anything that is overly serious or melodramatic – melodrama being tantamount to one of the cardinal sins here in the Land of the Nice. Go to a sappy Hollywood flick in Iceland and you will notice endless snickering where, by design, there should be tears. The Icelanders just cannot take anything too seriously – least of all themselves. Indeed, taking yourself too seriously is considered a minor crime in Iceland, and instantly makes you a legitimate target for all sorts of ridicule. Seriously. You'll want to trust me on this one.

Whenever something serious happens that by rights should make a big, traumatic dent in the national psyche, the Icelanders will almost always find ways to laugh about it. It's their way of coping. Case in point: after the 2008 economic meltdown,

the Icelandic nation was embroiled in much social turmoil and unrest. Yet on national TV every Saturday evening, one of the country's best-known comedy troupes, Spaugstofan, picked apart all the dreadful details of the collapse that we had wallowed in during the week and served it up as comic ingenuity. The nation was in stitches. We roared with laughter at our own predicament, and at the caricatures of the people who had brought us down.

Soon after that we had municipal elections, and one of Iceland's best-known comedians, Jón Gnarr, set up a faux-election campaign to poke fun at our elected officials and the staid and worn out system that had brought us to the brink of disaster. To everyone's amazement, his pseudo-campaign garnered a big following. Long story short, a few weeks later Jón Gnarr's "Best Party" (slogan: All kinds of things for idiots) had won the municipal elections, and Gnarr himself was mayor of Reykjavík. He became so popular that he likely would have won a second term had he not stepped down of his own accord.

Satire is something that the oppressed have often used in order to cope with circumstances over which they are powerless. You might say the Icelanders have been laughing through their tears for the past eight centuries or so, as they soldiered on, tyrannized and downtrodden, in a harsh and unforgiving climate, under the heel of a ruthless elite. *Hláturinn lengir lífið*, the Icelanders say – "laughter prolongs your life". There is no doubt in my mind that laughter has not only prolonged the life of individual Icelanders, but has been a source of formidable strength for the nation as a whole.

6
GOING FOR IT

One of the great things about living in Iceland is that it is so easy to make things happen.

The Icelanders tend to have enthusiasm in spades and are usually really keen to participate in fun projects. They're super motivated. I don't know what it is that makes them so receptive to that sort of thing, but suspect it's a combination of factors – not the least of which is that it's so easy to make connections and get things launched.

Let's say you have an idea for something – a band, an arts project, a small business or whatever – someone you know will almost certainly know a bass player, or have a rehearsal space, or know how to get funding. Or they'll know someone who knows someone. And if they don't, you can always just pick up the phone and call someone you think might be able to help. Most people in Iceland are really receptive to that sort of thing, and no one thinks you're weird for doing it.

Bands, theatre ensembles, dance troupes, publishing collectives, think tanks … ventures like those thrive in Iceland. And none of it would be possible without a healthy dose of what the Icelanders call *kæruleysi*, definitely one of the operating words when describing the Icelandic national character. It's a hard concept to translate literally … I suspect the word is derived from the English "careless" (n.b. I have nothing to back this up), but whereas the English word has a slightly negative connotation when describing a person, in Icelandic it is used for someone who is spontaneous, who just goes for things without thinking too much about the consequences. As such it has a definite positive slant. *Bara að slá þessu upp í kæruleysi*, the Icelanders say, meaning "I'm not going to be held back by worry – I'm going for it".

Obviously there are two sides to the kæruleysi coin – there's the side that throws caution to the wind, and there's the side that throws caution to the wind without thinking too much about the consequences for other people. (See also section on Icelanders' driving habits, and everything that has ever been written about the Icelandic economic meltdown.)

7
PATRO, MATRO ...
OR BOTH?

To the uninitiated, Icelandic surnames can be totally confusing. In a typical Icelandic family, the mother, father, son and daughter will all have a different last name. Which has raised some eyebrows in foreign lands, at hotel receptions, for example.

Icelanders use patronyms (or, increasingly, matronyms), which were common to the Nordic countries around the time that Iceland was settled. As you may know, that's where all those Johnsons, Petersons, Jacksons, et al stem from.

Under this system, a child's last name is made by taking the first name of the father or mother, and adding *-son* if it's a boy, or *-dóttir* if it's a girl. Taking the father's name, the patronym, is more common, though matronyms have been gaining in popularity in more recent years.

It works like this: let's say there's a couple named Jón and Guðrún. They have a son named Karl, and a daughter named Katrín. If the kids (or, well, their parents) decide to use patronyms, the son's full name will be Karl Jónsson, and the daughter's full name Katrín Jónsdóttir.

If, however, they decide to use matronyms, their names would be Karl Guðrúnarson and Katrín Guðrúnardóttir.

If Karl has children, his son will be Karlsson (assuming he's using patronyms) and his daughter will be Karlsdóttir. When Katrín has children (and assuming they're using matronyms), they will be Katrínarson and/or Katrínardóttir.

So children do not have the same last name as their parents, because they have their parents' first names as the first part of their last names.

Meanwhile, some people decide to use both patro- and matronyms, presumably in honour of both their parents. This is something that has only caught on in the last few years, though, and it is still pretty rare. In that case they would call themselves, say, Karl Guðrúnar- og Jónsson (Karl, son of Guðrún and Jón), or simply Karl Guðrúnar Jónsson.

And in case you are wondering why the mother and father will have different names, well, that is because Icelandic women do not change their names when they get married. It's not a thing in Iceland. That said, foreigners who marry Icelanders are legally permitted to take the last name of their husband or wife if they so choose, even if that last name is a matro- or patronym. Example: Jane Guðmundsson. I have seen a number of such names that have been adopted by female partners of Icelandic men, but curiously, none by the male partners of Icelandic women. But surely it is only a matter of time before we see a name like Jack Gunnarsdóttir, don't you think?

8
AS FOR FAMILY NAMES ...

Meanwhile, some people in Iceland are not *-son* or *-dóttir* but rather have family names. What's up with that?

Glad you asked. Yes indeed, family names do exist in Iceland. Most of them are leftovers from the past, when Iceland was a colony of Denmark, and have been handed down through the generations. Many hail from the Danish aristocracy, and as such still carry a vaguely elitist air. In fact, in the early 20th century, as Iceland was sloughing off its colonial past, family names became very fashionable and people were making up their own names willy-nilly (sort of like the phone book professions of today). After a while it all became a bit too much, so a law was passed to ban family names in order to preserve the old tradition. But in true Icelandic fashion people did not pay much attention to the law and just carried on being creative

with the ol' family names. This went on right up until 1991, when family names were declared absolutely, unequivocally illegal, on punishment of being drowned in a bubbling hot spring. (Just kidding. About the drowning.)

Today, family names are inherited – for example the daughter of Jón Thorarensen will be Jensína Thorarensen, and her children will be, say, Karl and Katrín Thorarensen – that is, if Jensína's children decide not to go with patronyms (yes, some people do eschew family names for more proletarian traditions).

Today, the only way for a new family name to be officially registered is if a foreign citizen moves to Iceland and/or has a child with an Icelandic partner. That child can then adopt the foreign parent's family name.

Also, if a woman marries a man with a family name, she can – by law – adopt her husband's name. But women rarely do, probably because the whole concept of changing your name is so alien to Icelandic women.

Incidentally, in case you were wondering, the five most common family names in Iceland are Thorarensen, Blöndal, Hansen, Olsen and Möller.

9
NICKING A NAME

Icelanders have long had a habit of giving people nicknames, which they call *viðurnefni*, or by-names. They've been doing it forever (or, well, since they arrived in Iceland). The Sagas and subsequent tales are filled with people who have nicknames, like for instance the formidable Hallgerður langbrók (Hallgerður long-pants; yes, really) – a name believed to have been formed in reference to her long legs. She is most famous for refusing to give her husband Gunnar á Hlíðarenda (Gunnar from Slope's End, aka the name of their farm) a lock of her hair when his enemies had him surrounded and the string of his bow broke, all because he had slapped her face a while back. The hair was for the bow, of course, so he could defend himself. Alas, because of her refusal, old Gunnar was killed. And that's what you call payback.

But I digress.

Other common nicknames from the old days are, for instance, Ríki/Ríka (literally: "the rich", used as a second name for women or men who were wealthy) and Flóki (literally "tangle" – probably reserved for men who had a full head of hair and no comb, therefore lots of tangles). Incidentally, Flóki is a proper Icelandic man's name now, approved

by the Name Committee and everything (more on that later).

Today the nickname tradition prevails, especially in small villages. A friend who grew up in a fishing village in the West Fjords says almost everyone there had a nickname, especially if their names were common, like Gunnar or Jón. This helped differentiate them from the next Gunnar or Jón. Also, some of those names could be pretty, um, incisive. For instance, there was a group of kids who earned the nickname Skand (i.e. Jói Skand, Anna Skand … I'm making these first names up) because some family members frequently got drunk and caused a scandal (the Icelandic word for scandal is *skandall*).

Meanwhile, one of the locals, known for his foxhunting prowess, acquired the name Ásgeir Rebbi – *rebbi* being a cutesy name for fox in Icelandic. This later became shortened to Rebb, and the name was subsequently also applied to his children, making them Sigga Rebb, Jói Rebb, and so on.

Another interesting nicknaming facet, my friend tells me, was an informal tradition of matronyms in the West Fjords, which is mostly made up of fishing villages. Kids were associated with their mothers because their fishermen fathers were away so much and so often. Here, too, nicknames were involved. A boy named Karl Jónsson, whose mother's name was Katrín, might then be called Kalli Kötu – Kalli being a nickname for Karl, and Kata being a nickname for Katrín (and Kötu being Kata in the genitive). Even though formally Karl would have a patronym, for all intents and purposes his mother was the head of the family, so the matronym would kick in on a colloquial basis.

Also Icelanders tend to give people nicknames – often folks who are in the news and have become household names. Methinks it harks back to taking people down a notch (like when the Icelanders laugh at those to whom they feel subordinate), though in this case it is usually done in a perfectly good-humoured manner. Example: Iceland's best-known astrologer, whose name is Gunnlaugur, is commonly referred to as Gulli stjarna, or "Gulli the Star". A well-known seismologist is referred to as Ragnar skjálfti, or "Ragnar the Tremor". A helicopter pilot who did brisk business flying with people over the 2010 volcanic eruptions is called Jón spaði, or "Jón the Blade". And so on.

There is also a curiously sardonic twist to this practice, in that sometimes the names will mean the exact opposite of that which is logical. An art conservator named Ólafur, who several years back exposed a major forgery scandal, was subsequently dubbed Óli falsari, or "Óli the Forger" – though obviously he had nothing to do with the actual forgery. Finnur Ingólfsson, a former politician and Central Bank director whose manner of attracting wealth has raised more than a few questions, and eyebrows, is frequently referred to as Finnur fátæki, or "Finnur the Pauper". The first is just meant to be funny-slash-absurd. The second probably falls into the "down-a-notch" category.

And in a homogenous country with a small population where the local news reaches pretty much everyone, we all get the joke.

10
PASSING NAMES

Iceland has a committee that approves or turns down names. People's names. Yup. It's called Mannanafnanefnd, literally "Human Name Committee".

This need for approval typically applies to names in which the parents want to get a little, shall we say, *creative* with the naming of their offspring. The reason why there are not many Icelandic equivalents of Blue Ivy, or North West, or Apple, or Sir, is that those sorts of names have to be passed by the name committee before they are officially bestowed upon the poor unsuspecting child.

Fascist? Perhaps. But consider: Icelandic is one complicated language (no news to many of you) and one of its more difficult features is that the nouns, as opposed to just the verbs, decline according to case. They change. Either their endings change, or the whole name changes.

Take the woman's name Hafdís. There are four different cases in Icelandic, so the name would change from Hafdís (nominative), to Hafdísi (accusative and dative), to Hafdísar (genitive). Similarly, the man's name Egill (nominative) changes to Egil (accusative), to Agli (dative), to Egils (genitive). All depending on how you use them in a sentence.

So the Human Name Committee, among other things, is tasked with making sure that the name in question declines properly in Icelandic. If it does, and is considered kosher (that is, if it is not Satan, Horsehair, or similar), it has a good chance of being passed by the Human Name Committee. If not, well, then something a tad more conventional is probably required.

Incidentally, the Human Name Committee is perpetually controversial, and talk of abolishing it pops up regularly. When this is written, in late 2018, a bill is pending in the Icelandic parliament that would do just that. Whether it is passed remains to be seen, but with rising immigration and foreign influences in Iceland, the pressure to abolish state approval or disapproval of names is only likely to grow.

11
APPLYING NAMES

Icelandic babies generally remain nameless for weeks or even months after they are born. This is because, after the birth, the proposed name of that child remains Top Secret. Only the parents know the name they plan to give their child, and

sometimes someone close to the child, say a grandparent – but even that's rare. People generally don't bother to ask the parents what the child's name is going to be, because usually they won't get an answer. Like everyone else they have to wait until the christening, which usually takes place a month or two (or four, or six) after the birth.

Until that time, the young child is simply known by some cutesy name of the family's choosing, like *litli* (little boy), *litla* (little girl), *prinsinn/prinsessan* (the prince/princess), *lilli/lilla*, or similar. Indeed, sometimes those cutesy names will stick with that person throughout their lives. I once knew a woman in her 80s who was always called Lilla by members of her family.

Formally, like while still in hospital (although Icelandic mothers are usually out on their tender perineums around 24 hours after giving birth), the child would be known as *drengur* (boy) or *stúlka* (girl) and then the last name – which, as you'll remember from a previous lesson, usually consists of a patronym – say "Jónsson" or "Jónsdóttir".

So again, nobody knows the name of the child until they show up at the christening, and the minister says, *Hvað á barnið að heita?* (What's the child to be named?) and the parents say: "Karlotta Jósefína Eleonora," or similar.

Which by then, of course, has already been passed by the Human Name Committee.

12
TRADITIONS IN NAMES

Just as it is relatively common in Anglo-Saxon countries for sons to be named after their fathers (example: Aubrey Pumpernickel III), it is relatively common for Icelanders to name their child after one of their parents.

Someone named Karl Jónsson, for instance, might name his son Jón, after his father. The son would then be named Jón Karlsson. If Jón then names his son (assuming he has a son at some point) Karl, after his father, his son would be named Karl Jónsson, exactly like the grandfather. (If you are reading this early in the morning, my apologies. Please go have two cups of coffee, then attempt it again.)

This would likely make the grandfather very proud. And happy.

Take me, for instance. I have the exact same name as my grandmother. Her name was Alda Sigmundsdóttir (OK, actually it was *Guðrún* Alda Sigmundsdóttir, but she always went by Alda) and she named her son Sigmundur, after her father.

He, in turn, named me Alda after his mother, so I have the same name as her.

My husband, too, has a daughter with the exact same name as his mother.

All of which is fine. When it's not fine is when a child's grandparent starts to exert pressure to have the child named after them. This happens. Seriously, some grandparents are so intent on having what the Icelanders call a little *nafna* or *nafni* (namesake) that they can get a little agitated (I'm being generous here) if, or when, a child is named after someone else. This can cause substantial strain in families, not least between the parents of the child, say if one parent wants to cave in to the demands of the grandparent, and the other parent does not.

Sometimes a grandparent will spend weeks or months wondering if the little angel is going to bear his or her name, and even expecting it to be so ... only to discover at the baptismal font that the child is being given another name entirely – which may even be the name of the *other* grandparent (gasp!).

To skirt this difficulty, many Icelandic parents wind up naming their child what the Icelanders call *út í loftið* or "into the air" – meaning that the child that is not named after anyone in particular, it just carries some name that the parents like ... or have purposely chosen so that no one's feelings would get hurt.

13
NAME VISITATIONS

If you think grandparents exerting pressure to have children named after them is strange – think again. Sometimes someone who is unrelated to the child will show up in a dream *að vitja nafns* – a phrase that is very difficult to translate, but which basically means, "to visit for a name". And that someone is almost always obliged.

This is a quirky little Icelandic superstition, and it goes something like this: if a pregnant woman dreams that someone comes to her and gives some sort of indication that the dream visit has to do with the unborn child, the Icelanders believe that the person is probably að vitja nafns. This is especially true if the person who appears in the dream is deceased. In a case like that, the parents will usually name the child after the dream apparition because it is considered bad luck not to comply. The child might fall victim to serious misfortune, or wind up handicapped in some way.

Though the superstitious element may not always be the overriding motivation, this practice is still very much today. Take for instance my husband's youngest daughter, Ragnheiður. When her mother was pregnant she had a dream in which a woman appeared who had been important to her as

a child. The woman's name was Ragnheiður and she was deceased. This Ragnheiður appeared quite stern in the dream, and had a red mark on her forehead, above the bridge of the nose. When Ragnheiður (husband's daughter) was born a few weeks later, she had a red mark *in exactly that same spot* on her face.

And so, they decided that the older Ragnheiður had been að vitja nafns, and decided to name the baby Ragnheiður after her.

14
TURNING A FOREIGN NAME NATIVE

It may shock you (or not) to learn that, until fairly recently, foreigners who took Icelandic citizenship were legally obliged to adopt an Icelandic name.

You couldn't just become a citizen of the Land of the Nice with a name like, say, Jim Jones, or Pol Pot, or Marilyn Monroe. Or even John Doe, for that matter.

You needed a down-home *Icelandic* name.

Granted, you were allowed to *add* a name somewhere in the middle. Example: Walter *Haraldur* Winterbottom. The powers-that-be generously allowed such a concession.

But then we entered the era of globalization and internationalization and all those other -izations, and this regulation came increasingly under fire. Because there were a lot of foreign people moving to Iceland, and some of them actually just wanted to be called, you know, *their name*, even if they opted to become Icelandic citizens.

So some people resolved to make these names as silly as possible, to highlight the absurdity of the whole undertaking. For instance there was this one guy from South America who changed his moniker from Carlos (or something) to Eilífur Friður. Both Eilífur and Friður are accepted Icelandic names – but put together, they mean Eternal Peace. How's that for a round of peaceful protest? His point, obviously, was to highlight how ridiculous the law was – and it may just have worked because soon afterward, the law was abolished. So you can now be called whatever you like (well, within limits – you still have to answer to the Human Name Committee) and nevertheless be an Icelandic citizen.

15
OF OPTIMISM

Even though they live on the edge of the inhabitable world with engulfing darkness for several months of the year, the Icelanders continue to score among the most optimistic people in the world.

Is it the fish? The fresh air? The cod liver oil? Natural selection? The copious amounts of anti-depressants they consume?

Nobody really knows.

However, one thing is sure: this character trait serves Icelanders well and has helped the nation cope with innumerable shocks, from volcanic eruptions, to famines, to a massive economic crisis. Whatever happens you can be sure that the Icelanders will seek the silver lining and soldier on, firmly believing that things will soon get better.

Indeed it is fascinating to observe how the Icelanders deal with trauma at a national level. Their initial reaction always seems to be to bond together. People who on regular days

will bicker and quarrel amongst themselves, suddenly become enormously supportive of each other. I've seen this happen in the aftermath of disasters such as snow avalanches and volcanic eruptions, or tragedies that capture the nation's attention.

Take, for example, the economic meltdown of 2008, which for the Icelanders was one of the most catastrophic events in recent history. Many people feared an onslaught of suicides in the wake of all the bankruptcies that ensued. Yet it turned out that the number of suicides actually declined. According to the Directorate of Health it was because the nation had bonded together, and people were closer and more supportive of each other than they had been in a very long time.

In other words, the optimism is probably a long-term survival strategy. After all, through the centuries of hardship and geographical isolation that the Icelandic nation has endured, defeat was not an option – it was stand together, fight together, or die. And fighting naturally incorporates optimism – after all, you have to believe there is something worth fighting for.

Mind you, this is just my own homegrown theory. A devil's advocate would probably ask why the other Nordic nations are not the same – why there isn't the same prevalence of optimism there. Or bring up the bloody family feuds in the Iceland of yore, where folks cut each other down willy-nilly for the stupidest reasons. To which I don't even pretend to have an answer.

16
THINGS
WORKING OUT

If there is one phrase that captures the Icelanders' innate sense of optimism better than any other, it is this:

Þetta reddast.

Þetta reddast should be emblazoned across the nation's coat of arms, for it is a phrase that captures the essence of the Icelandic national character perhaps better than any other – their optimism, their irreverence, their faith, their tenacity. It also happens to be a phrase that the Icelanders use constantly.

Þetta reddast basically means: *This will all work out one way or another.*

Just lost your job? *Þetta reddast.* No money in the bank? *Þetta reddast.* Economy just melted down? *Þetta reddast.* Volcano just spewed ash all over your arable land? *Þetta reddast líka.*

I love the phrase þetta reddast. To me, it incorporates a profound philosophy. Because when things are totally dark and you really can't see the way out, often the best thing you can do is let go and trust that somehow, some way, things will work out for the best. And the amazing thing is that … they almost always do.

17
WORK OR CHEAT

The Icelanders are a hardy bunch with a seriously intense work ethic. It's written into their DNA. Survival in the sorts of conditions the Icelanders have endured over the centuries would not have been possible without some hard-core work. *Harkan sex*, say the Icelanders, which literally translated means, um, "harshness six", but which figuratively translated means "yes this is freaking harsh, but damn it you will just have to get on with it!" Or something to that effect.

In today's Iceland, being a hard worker is considered one of the supreme virtues. People who are industrious and work hard – who are *dugleg*, as the Icelanders say – are admired and revered.

But being industrious is not the only thing coded into the Icelanders' hereditary material. So is working in spurts. Just like in the old days when the boats came in with the catch and everyone and their grandmother had to go down to the harbour and work overtime to preserve it. Even the schools were closed. This could go on for a week, or even longer. Everyone pitched in to ensure the survival of the community.

Today "the community" has generally been replaced by "the company". The Icelanders call this manner of working *tarnir* (*törn* in the singular). *Ég er í vinnutörn* they will say, meaning "I am in a work spurt". And because working is such a great

virtue and beyond reproach, this also means: "I am hereby legally excused from all my responsibilities because I am working so hard". Everyone understands if you are in a törn.

The downside of all this is that most Icelanders feel vaguely (or considerably, or seriously) guilty if they are not working – evenings and weekends included. If they are doing something so frivolous as *relaxing* on the weekends, say.

In fact, every Icelander knows that life in Iceland is different from life abroad because abroad most people take the weekends off *and it is actually considered acceptable*. Whereas in Iceland, it's considered cheating.

18
BEING AT THE LAST MINUTE

Some people have this image of the Icelanders being like their Scandinavian brothers and sisters, doing everything really efficiently and on time.

Ah, the fallacy!

The Icelanders are the Southern Europeans of North

Europe. The family is central in their lives. They like to put things off (*mañana*). They're frequently late. Their buses don't run on time.

And they do pretty much everything at the last minute. Whether it is showing up for an appointment or a movie, delivering a work project, signing up for a workshop, booking a summer holiday … whatever it is, it's pretty much guaranteed that the person in question will wait until the eleventh hour to get it done.

The Icelanders are completely aware of this little quirk. *Ég er auðvitað á síðustu stundu með þetta*, they will say, meaning: "Of course I'm doing this at the last minute." *Of course*, because every Icelander knows that this is the way things are done in Iceland.

I have pondered why this is. Maybe it is in some way connected to the tarnir thing. Maybe the Icelanders leave everything until the last minute so they can wind up in a törn, because the tarnir are virtuous and fun in a vaguely masochistic way. Plus they give you a sense of belonging.

Or perhaps the Icelanders are just a nation of adrenaline junkies, and get a kick out of the stress inherent in doing everything at the last minute. No, seriously.

Or it could go back to the independence issue. The Icelanders put off making a decision or commitment until the very last minute because not doing so could restrict their independence in some way. And that, to the average Icelander, is the cruellest of fates.

19
THE BUSY LITTLE COUNTRY THAT COULD

Directly related to the work ethic and tarnir is the Icelandic tendency to be busy all the darn time. Foreigners who move to Iceland often remark on this, finding it incredibly hard to pin Icelandic friends down for a drink or coffee because they're always rushing around like crazy.

This perpetual tumult in which most Icelanders seem to live to is so typical that they are wont to greet one another with the phrase: *Brjálað að gera?*, meaning "Are you insanely busy?" This tends to be delivered in jovial, backslapping fashion, as if to say: "I can see that your life is completely and utterly hectic, and I applaud you for it because surely it means you are uncommonly dugleg and doing something highly important."

I have sometimes wondered if the Icelanders really are more insanely busy than their counterparts in other countries, or if they are just trying to seem busy in order to gain admiration and respect. I have determined, solely through observations and no studies whatsoever, that as a rule they are legitimately very busy. But why? How is it that people in other countries

can find time for a leisurely cup of coffee with friends, or a beer after work, while the Icelanders are always running ragged, in a constant race against the clock?

I took my musings to Facebook, as one does, and before long the answer was deposited neatly in the comments. At the time of writing, Iceland has a population of 350 thousand people. Of those, there are 232 thousand between the ages of 15 and 64 – an age group that might conceivably be paying taxes (in Iceland young people 15 and older very often work alongside their school studies). I am inclined, however, to deduct 30 thousand people from that figure, for adolescents who are not working, people who are disabled, and – not least – the shameless financial moguls who always find ways to avoid paying their communal fees. That leaves roughly 200 thousand people who must generate enough tax revenue to run an entire society, with all its various sectors, systems and infrastructure – health care, education, government, arts and culture, communications, law enforcement, transport, and so forth. And in order to do so, members of the "middle class" – which, as a social stratum, is gradually disappearing – need to work two jobs to make ends meet.

Indeed, when you think about it, it really is phenomenal that a nation the size of Iceland is able to carry on in a semi-functional manner. Some would (and do) argue that it really cannot, and that the reason for the insidious and wide-reaching corruption in Icelandic society is that the nation is too small to adequately govern itself. But that is another discussion entirely, which shall not be broached on these pages.

20
CURSE OF THE CANINE CLEANERS

If you have visited Iceland over the past decade or so, you may have noticed a good number of dogs about. Not that this would be particularly noteworthy to people who are used to dogs in their local surroundings, of course – but in Iceland, this proliferation of canines is quite a new trend. As recently as twenty years ago, it was rare to see people out walking their dogs in Iceland.

Given how common a sight dogs are now, you might surmise that the Icelanders are a nation of dog lovers. Alas, no. Antipathy towards canines is deeply rooted in the Icelandic national psyche. A large proportion of Icelanders just *does not like dogs*. They distrust them. They are afraid of them. They do not want them off-leash anywhere. And they absolutely do not want them in enclosed public spaces, like banks, shops, offices, on public transport, or anywhere else.

So why all this hate against man's best friend?

Well, I'm pretty sure it harks back to the old days when the

Icelandic population lived in turf houses and hygiene was a rather, shall we say, *alien* concept. In those days it was the job of the farm dogs to clean the *askar* – wooden bowls with lids that were the primary vessels from which to eat. Every Icelander had his or her own *askur* (singular of askar) and when people finished eating, the askur would be handed to the nearest dog, who would proceed to lick it clean.

Of course what people did not know is that dogs tended to carry tapeworm, which was then passed on to the humans and became a major source of disease, and even death.

When it was discovered that the cleaning services provided by the household pooches weren't all they were cracked up to be, dogs were instantly branded as filthy, disease-bearing beasts. Soon after that the urban drift began. Icelanders moved into towns and cities and sought to dissociate themselves from their humble origins in the turf houses, which many considered a humiliating testimony to their colonial past. The business of the dogs and the tapeworm was one such shameful association, and dogs, it was commonly agreed, had no place in town life. They belonged in the country with the peasants.

In fact, they belonged there so much that it was considered necessary to pass a law to keep them there. And so, in 1924, a ban on dogs came into force in Reykjavík. Under this ban, no canines were permitted within the city limits. At first many folks ignored this statute (Icelanders and their independence, remember), which led to incidents such as law enforcement showing up on people's doorsteps, dragging their dogs out

into the street, and shooting them in front of their owners.

I'll leave you to ponder that for a moment.

In 1984 the Reykjavík City Council bowed to mounting pressure and agreed to grant a temporary exemption from the law. That exemption stayed in effect for four years, at which time a referendum took place on whether or not dogs should be allowed in the city. Out of more than 68 thousand voters only some nine thousand turned up at the polls, and the proposal to lift the dog ban was voted down with a 60 percent majority.

It was not until 2002 that the ban on dogs in Reykjavík was finally amended, permitting people to keep dogs in the Reykjavík area. Note that I say "amended" – the ban on dogs is still in full effect, with dog ownership only allowed if certain criteria and obligations are met. These include the payment of an annual license fee that in comparison with other countries is absurdly high. A quick online search reveals that a dog license in most US states cost USD 15-30 in 2018, depending on whether or not the dog was spayed/neutered. In the UK and Ireland it cost the equivalent of some USD 17. In Iceland, the annual license fee is USD 196, though a 50 percent discount is provided after the first year of registration if the dog has attended a certified obedience training course that costs around USD 300.

Despite this hefty annual fee, dog owners receive precious few services in return for their outlay of cash. The city provides a handful of off-leash areas within its limits, but they

are few and far between, and almost all are the size of a small backyard, enclosed by a chicken-wire fence – certainly not big enough for a dog to run around in, say, or chase a ball. Dog-catchers have become virtually unnecessary with the growing might of Facebook, since dogs that are lost or found are usually returned to their owners by way of a few strategic posts and shares. City authorities, when asked to justify the license fee, can provide few answers, while dog owners grumble that their pooches are being taxed to fund other, completely unrelated, projects within the municipal system. Which they probably are.

21
DEATH BY DOG

So today, what with scientific awareness, plus a legal decree that all dogs must be de-wormed at least once a year, the tape-worm scourge is no longer the main issue underpinning the Icelanders' dogophobia. Something else has taken its place: the dreaded *allergies*.

See, those who still argue vehemently that dogs have no place in city life tend to do so on the grounds that *there are people with allergies*. To hear this group speak one cannot help but envision scores of people in any given public space dropping to the ground and clutching at their throats the moment a canine enters the vicinity. The arguments tend to be delivered with such passion that one might believe Icelanders to be uncommonly susceptible to a particularly dangerous, and potentially fatal, strain of dog allergy. For, as the pro-dog contingent is wont to point out, even though dogs are allowed in many a public space in other countries, there seems to be a notable absence of fatalities caused by being in close proximity to one.

All that being said, as dog ownership becomes increasingly trendy in Iceland (let's face it: dogs, especially purebred ones, have become somewhat of a fashion statement, and the Icelanders *love* their trends, more on that later), the most stringent dog-curbing regulations (see what I did there?) are gradually being relaxed. In 2018, for example, the Reykjavík city council voted to allow dogs and cats on city buses, much to the jubilation of the pro-dog squadron. Surprisingly, in the few months since this change took effect, no one has died of an allergic reaction on a city bus. So surely within a decade or two, dogs will be a normal part of urban life in Iceland, much as they are in other civilized countries.

22
THAT BIZARRE EMAIL FRUSTRATION

If you are a visitor to Iceland, chances are you have tried to contact Icelandic businesses or institutions via email, and been equal parts incredulous and frustrated when they didn't respond. In fact, you may not even have received an acknowledgement of your request.

Be advised: you are not alone. The list of frustrated foreigners who have tried to correspond with Icelanders via email is about the length of one of those transatlantic telecommunications cables connecting North America to Europe.

Even in cases where these people want to buy something from Icelandic businesses, *i.e. want to part with their money*, many Icelanders can't seem to get their act together to respond to a simple email.

This is a totally crazymaking aspect of Icelandic society. For some reason, Icelanders don't respond to emails. This is not true of everyone, mind you – if that were the case, Icelandic society would be pretty dysfunctional (oh, wait...). But it does apply to some people. A lot of people, in fact.

I know some non-Icelanders who have wondered if it is because they are foreign. Racking their brain for answers, they wonder if this strange conduct can be attributed to the language barrier, or plain old xenophobia.

Strange as it seems, I almost wish it could be. Then we'd have an explanation, at least. But alas, this bizarre affliction also affects those of us who speak Icelandic, even where the establishment or person concerned is just a few streets away.

Dealing with email, especially where there is some kind of request involved, involves a certain level of commitment. It means potentially entering into a business relationship, or, conversely, turning down a business relationship. Ergo, making a decision, or commitment – the Icelanders' main source of anxiety. And so, in many cases it's probably just easier to ignore that email and pretend it didn't arrive.

Mind you, this is just my little homegrown theory and I have no idea if it is correct. I do know, though, that doing business – or *trying* to do business – with the Icelanders can be utterly exasperating. I tend to send two emails, maybe a third if I've had even a cursory response, and if we're not getting anywhere by that point, I give up. It's not worth the aggravation, and there are almost certainly opportunities elsewhere.

23
THE UPSIDE OF NOT PLANNING AHEAD

One quirk the Icelanders have is a serious problem planning things in advance. They like to do things on the spur of the moment. To be spontaneous, like.

This can be a really endearing quality, really creative and fun. It can also be horribly frustrating. With many Icelanders I've known, getting them to commit to something six months or a year down the line is like trying to pull teeth from a horse with a pair of tweezers.

My husband and I belonged to an online home exchange site for a while, and we frequently started getting requests in September or October for the following summer. That just boggles the mind of most Icelanders. For them, planning something that early is insane. I mean, think of all the things that could happen in the interim – your goldfish could die, or

your house burn down, or a volcano go off. Hell, you might even get a better offer!

This dread of planning could be attributed to the fear of losing independence. It might have deeper and more complex roots, though, hailing back to the days when nothing could be planned ahead of time on account of the climate. In the Iceland of yore, life was all about flexibility and spontaneity. If you planned to go out fishing and the weather suddenly turned bad, you simply had to make other plans. If you planned to go to church on Sunday, and the weather turned out to be warm and dry, plans were cancelled so everyone could go out in the fields and make hay. If you planned to go to school but suddenly a ship came in with a belly full of fish, the school was closed and all the kids were sent down to the harbour to preserve the catch.

And so, while the lack of advance planning can be frustrating, it can also be great. Spontaneity and flexibility are excellent qualities, potentially resulting in wonderfully creative vibes and quick decision-making. And those things can be incredibly valuable, as long as they're channelled in the right direction. It's when you're trying to pin someone down to a specific time and place – and not succeeding – that they can drive you crazy.

24
ICELAND, WHERE TRAFFIC LAWS ARE GUIDELINES

When God came down to Earth to hand out driving skills and refinement, I'm pretty sure He drove right past the Icelanders.

The Icelanders are terrible drivers. I cannot emphasize this point enough.

Before moving back to Iceland, I had lived in one metropolis (Toronto), one country where the highways have no speed limit (Germany), sojourned in a town with six-lane traffic circles (Valencia, Spain), and even mastered driving in the UK, where everything is backwards, with a six-month-old baby in the front seat.

I considered myself pretty invincible in the driving department.

Alas, none of this would prepare me for motoring in the Land of the Nice. I had been back for

less than a year when I was rear-ended on a traffic ramp and wound up in a neck brace. Two years later I was involved in another accident, this time as a passenger in a car that ran a red light and hit another at around 60 km an hour. This exacerbated my earlier injury, and gave rise to the trafficphobia that makes me probably the most annoying passenger on the planet (just ask my husband).

You see, for many Icelanders, traffic laws are entirely optional. In fact, traffic laws are not really laws at all. They're more like ... guidelines.

Take indicator lights, for instance. Icelanders use them *very* sparingly, if at all. Often they'll put them on in the middle of a turn (as in: look! I'm turning!) or right after they've turned (I just made a turn!). Indicators are also considered superfluous when changing lanes or pulling into a parking space. In fact, if you plan to parallel park and use your indicator to make this clear, it will normally just confuse the hell out of the driver behind you – who will, almost without exception, be driving right on your ass.

Red lights are a chapter unto themselves. Most Icelanders do not view them as a command to stop their motor vehicle immediately, but rather as a mere suggestion to stop before another car rams into them from the side. In other words, as long as the light has *just* turned red, it's OK to put the pedal to the metal and proceed through at high speed. (I am *not* joking about this, so beware.) And if it's in the evening, when there aren't *that* many cars around, the red light tends to serve the same sort of function as an illuminated stop sign: drivers will stop, cast around, and if no cars are coming, proceed through.

Also, visitors should be advised that most Icelandic drivers do not stop at pedestrian crossings by default (as in, step out onto those white zebra lines at your own risk), they drive in whatever lane they damn well please (as in, very very slow in the passing lane), pass on the right (because there are slow cars in the passing lane), don't observe speed limits (80 km in a 50 km zone = normal), have never heard of parallel parking (note all those cars stuck diagonally into parking spaces with

their rears out in the road) and generally just park their cars wherever there is a free piece of pavement (because parking laws, like traffic laws, are, you know, guidelines).

In fact, it's a mystery why Icelandic authorities don't just step up traffic supervision and hire more parking attendants. They'd be able to develop that tourism infrastructure (more toilets! better roads!) in no time. Really: no time at all.

25
THAT CURIOUS AVERSION TO SIGNAGE

Somewhat related to the above is the bizarre Icelandic tendency not to put up road signs. It is almost like Icelandic road authorities expect everyone to know where everything is all the time.

Like many other things in the Icelandic national psyche, I believe this reflects the insularity of the nation – the presumption that everyone is like everyone else and should therefore

know where everything is, simply by instinct. Or DNA coding.

Let's say you're driving along the highway and looking for the road to somewhere. You'll keep your eyes peeled, perhaps expecting there to be a sign to notify you of an upcoming turn. Which would probably be the norm in most other countries – but not in Iceland. In this country the sign will most probably appear about five metres before you're due to make the turn … so you miss it.

Indeed, I sometimes wonder how tourists manage to find anything in Iceland. How they manage to make their flights back home, for instance, and don't just stay lost up on some heath somewhere, driving around in circles trying to find their way back to the southwest corner of the island. I mean, it's hard enough for us locals to find our way to parts of Breiðholt (suburb) – and we *live* here.

And this is by no means limited to locations or sites. The same goes for road works. In Iceland there will typically be a sign warning you of construction on the road a split second before it narrows into a single lane. Or of a pothole in the road two seconds before you land in it. Hell, even manholes will be left open sometimes with nothing more than a thin plank over them and gaping gaps on each side.

I've often thought it might be easier to have a sign *after* the fact. As in "you've just landed in a pothole, schmuck" or "your car is now officially f*cked". It would most probably result in a lot less panic than the system they have in place now.

26
IN ICELAND, WOMEN ARE MEN

You know that annoying problem in English when you don't know whether to refer to a person of unspecified gender as "he" or "she"?

As in: "The teacher wrote his/her name on the board before speaking to the class that he/she would be teaching that year".

The Icelanders don't have that problem.

This is because an official committee appointed by the Icelandic authorities declared that all people in Iceland shall be referred to as "men" and use the pronoun "he". Irrespective of gender. On the grounds that, in Icelandic, "men" is synonymous with "human being".

And so, whenever there is a person of unspecified gender in a sentence, that person is automatically a "he". Just, you know, in case you're ever confused.

On the other hand, you then get that pesky noun confusion.

Icelandic has three different genders for nouns: masculine, feminine and neuter.

Now, take the word *ráðherra*, which is a noun meaning "cabinet minister". Literally translated it means "ruling mister" (no, I am not making this up) and is, of course, of masculine gender.

However, female cabinet ministers are also called *ráðherrar* (ruling misters), and are referred to as "he" when a pronoun is used. To an outsider this can be extremely confusing … and, truth be told, it feels a bit odd to us natives, as well. Let's say someone is writing a news item about the prime minister, who happens to be female. It might read: "The prime minister re-iterated his words from earlier in the day." The fact that the ráðherra is a woman is irrelevant – she's still referred to as a "he". Because in Iceland she is a man – even if she's a woman.

27
WERY WERY KIND.
WERY KIND.

Icelandic doesn't have the letter "w" in its alphabet, which probably accounts for the fact that most Icelanders can't tell the difference between "w" and "v".

I should qualify that. They can usually hear the difference, if pressed. That is, if you spell it out for them and ask them to listen carefully. Whether they can then enunciate the "w" sound is another matter.

If they have to say a sentence that has both "v" and "w" sounds in it, it usually gets all mixed up. "Walking through the valley while vomiting vicious venom" can sound disastrous coming from the mouth of an Icelander. (Or, well, anyone, for that matter.)

The Icelanders tend to have that same problem with "sh", which usually comes out sounding just like an "s" – as in "see" instead of "she". "She sells sea shells by the sea shore" will come out of an Icelander's mouth as "see sells see sells by the see sore" ... and they really won't be able to figure out why this is a tongue-twister.

28
HOW ABOUT THAT NARCISSISTIC PARTY BEHAVIOUR?

Here's a somewhat prickly subject, and I would like to begin by saying that it certainly does not apply to all Icelanders I have met (but definitely to many).

They are hopeless at the art of conversation.

Let's say you're at a party. In most societies you will *converse* with people at that party. Meaning you ask a person something, they respond, they ask you something back, you respond, and so on. You have a *conversation*. An exchange, in which each party is interested (or at least pretends to be interested) in the views and opinions of the other.

Meanwhile, many Icelanders seem to have the idea that a conversation means droning on about themselves while looking right through you. When they do pause, they do not ask or wait for your opinion. Sometimes they'll wander off without another word. Frequently they'll just stare off into the distance. Anything but show that they're interested in you.

Then, if you do proffer an opinion, they'll go "a-ha, a-ha, a-ha" and continue looking right through you, until they find

a point they can latch on to that allows them to start talking about themselves all over again. Sometimes while you are in the middle of a sentence.

For instance, a while back I was at a big dinner. I sat at a table with a handful of people I didn't know well, and conversation was sparse. I tried to strike up a conversation with the person next to me. She answered every question I asked quite willingly – where do you work, how long have you been working there, yada yada – but the conversation was limited to me asking the questions. She asked nothing in return. Not a thing. Even when we discovered we shared a common interest in hiking I tried to get her involved by asking things like whether she preferred to use poles or not. She answered – but was not interested in further discussing poles, nor anything else relating to this common ground we had.

This is not an anomaly. I've observed scenarios like this over and over. For the longest time I thought it was down to me – that it was because I was so profoundly uninteresting. Eventually I wrote about it on my blog – hesitantly – and discovered that other expats (though I'm not strictly an expat, of course – but, you know) had experienced the very same thing.

I've sometimes wondered whether the Icelanders are raised to think it's rude to ask questions about others – whether the society is so profoundly insular that you just don't pry into others' affairs, however innocuously. But by that same logic, they presumably wouldn't want to open themselves too much, either – and that certainly does not seem to be a problem.

29
NO APOLOGIES, WE'RE ICELANDIC

You know how it is in most countries. You bump into someone, you say "excuse me". You burp, you say "excuse me". You pass wind, you say "excuse me".

In Iceland, this rarely happens. (The "excuse me" part.)

You actually sort of get used to it. I don't curse under my breath anymore when someone brushes up against me, or accidentally elbows me so that my drink spills down the front of my dress, or knocks my arm so that my glass hits my mouth and I wind up with a chipped tooth.

It's a cultural thing, and I blithely accept it.

However, there is one thing the Icelanders do that makes me want to scream from its sheer rudeness. It is this: let's say two people are talking, and a third person comes up and needs a word with one of those two. That person will *not* approach with a polite "excuse me" before directing his or her question to the intended recipient. He or she will simply barge into the middle of the conversation and ask the question *more loudly* than whoever is talking at the time.

And it works! I have never, ever met an Icelander who sees

anything wrong with this practice. They will, without fail, interrupt the conversation, even in mid-sentence, and direct their attention to the person who has so rudely commanded it. They'll even wander off without another word, leaving you hanging there in the middle of the exchange like it is the most normal thing in the world.

30
THE INVALUABLE SOCIAL FUNCTION OF THE HOT TUBS

The British have their pubs. The Turks have their teahouses. The French have their cafés. The Icelanders have their hot tubs.

For the Icelanders, hot tubs serve a very important social function. It's where people go for rest and relaxation and also where they discuss current events and social affairs of prime importance. And like the British have their favourite pubs and the French their favourite cafés, the Icelanders will have their favourite tubs. Some people will meet in the same hot tub for

years, at the same time every day or every week. Some begin their day that way, as early as 6:30 am, when most pools in the Reykjavík area throw open their doors.

A few years ago I sometimes found myself in the middle of a bunch of old timers that hung out in the Jacuzzi at the Laugardalslaug pool. They were retired seafarers who – in true Icelandic pre-economic-meltdown fashion – had turned to playing the stock market.

In the first week post-meltdown, with everyone scrambling to make sense of what had happened, I found myself in the tub. Predictably it was bubbling over with nervous energy. I learned a lot that day. For example: that I should immediately pull all my money out of the money market fund set up at my bank. A piece of advice freely proffered by an elderly gentleman in leopard patterned swim trunks.

I did that the very next day. As a result I was one of the very few people who did not lose a substantial chunk of my savings in the bank collapse. And quite frankly I would opt to have my financial advice delivered in a soothing, caressing hot tub any day, whether the country is embroiled in a financial meltdown or not.

31
BEWARE THE WRATH OF THE SHOWER POLICE

So if you are a visitor to Iceland and head to an Icelandic swimming pool hoping to score some free financial advice, please be advised that *you must shower naked*.

We Icelanders love our swimming pools. And we especially love them *clean*. That is why every single Icelander is taught to shower thoroughly *without a swimsuit* before going into any pool. And, yep, that means standing in the showers with lots of other people and soaping those parts of your body most prone to (um, how to put this delicately...) *bacterial infestation*. More specifically: hair, armpits, crotch and feet (ok, confession: no one ever washes their hair before going in the pool. *But everything else*). All of which is helpfully illustrated on posters hung in the changing rooms at any public pool.

I know, I know. The nekkid angle poses problems for a lot of visiting people. All those tourists out there not used to parading around in the buff, and who try to cheat by leaving their swimsuits on and just, you know, *rinsing*.

Tsk.

Enter the shower police, that garrison of Proper Hygiene, who, if they see you rinsing, will walk right up to you and order you to *take those bottoms off and lather up proper, you hear?* And even if they miss it, you can be sure that the Icelanders in the crowd will be watching, and will either take matters into their own hands or tip off the police.

Think I'm kidding? I am not.

Yes, I know it may seem really weird to some people to be all exposed like that. But, seriously, in Iceland … nobody cares. Until you *don't* shower naked, that is. By keeping that bathing suit on you will attract far more attention than any amount of cellulite or exotic waxing ever would.

32
REYKJAVÍK
NIGHTLOOT

If you're visiting Iceland and want to meet the locals, perhaps you'll opt for a night on the town.

After all, you may remember how Reykjavík used to be touted as the hip and cool capital of the world, as epitomized by its rowdy nightlife.

Reykjavík's rambunctious party scene is still going strong and it's not getting any more sophisticated with age. Let's face it: most Icelanders who go out on the weekends go out to get plastered. In Iceland this means going all wild and crazy. Dancing on tables, singing (or shouting) at the top of your lungs, doing shots until you're horizontal on the floor, stumbling around on Laugavegur vomiting into the gutter, you know, cool stuff like that.

The biggest nights for partying are Friday and Saturday, although Thursday has been gaining momentum of late. Now, one thing that confuses a lot of visitors is that most Icelanders don't go out until well after midnight. This is because booze is so freaking expensive, especially at the bars, so people tend to tank up at home (or at parties) before heading out.

This is also why you'll typically see lost-looking tourists wandering up and down Laugavegur on Friday and Saturday evenings, wondering *where da party at?*

As for closing hours, they have been an ever-shifting case of trial and error for Reykjavík authorities. A few years ago they were set at 3 am. This meant that people started showing up downtown around midnight and spilled out into the streets about three hours later. There the party had a habit of continuing, particularly in the summer when it was bright daylight in the middle of the night and no one had any pressing need to go to sleep. This gave rise to all kinds of pesky problems (aggravated physical assault, knife fights, the logistics of transporting thousands of people out of the area at once) so the powers-that-be figured the best way to solve them would be to let bars stay open longer.

Unfortunately this led to *other* irksome problems (people getting pumped on crystal meth so they could party all night long, residents in the area not getting a moment's rest on weekends, etc.) so then the law was changed again. These days it is hard to get a handle on exactly when establishments close in downtown Reykjavík, as it seems to be determined by location

(residential vs. commercial streets), day of the week (week-day vs. weekend), and the preference of the owners. Generally, though, the more popular clubs and bars stay open until 4:30 am, which is the cut-off point according to city bylaws.

This unhinged party scene has also given rise to another nasty problem, namely unbridled looting. Reykjavík nightlife is the Wild West, especially on weekends, and the amount of theft that goes on is nothing short of ridiculous. Jackets, coats, purses, cell phones, scarves ... in short, anything not expressly attached to someone's body is fair game. Indeed, in some establishments there have been reports of people entering without a coat or jacket, and exiting a while later wearing up to three at the same time.

So a word of caution: go partying by all means, but keep your wits about you, your drinks covered, and your belongings close.

33
AND WITH THAT, WE SEGUE INTO THE ALCOHOL PROBLEM

Given the Icelanders' zeal for partying, it is perhaps not surprising that Alcoholics Anonymous is a major social force in Iceland. In a country of 350 thousand people there are more than 300 different AA meetings per week nationwide. That's one for approximately every thousand inhabitants.

AA first broke ground in the Land of the Nice in 1954. It gained serious momentum in the 1970s when a number of people went for rehab in the US and came back on a mission: to help facilitate alcoholism recovery in Iceland. They subsequently formed an association called SÁÁ – Samtök áhugafólks um áfengisvandann, literally: The Association of People Interested in the Alcohol Problem (can't get much more prosaic than that), and set up a hospital and several rehab centres that specialized in alcohol treatment. Today SÁÁ is a key player in matters relating to addiction recovery, and though it is not

formally associated with AA, the two work together to help treat alcoholism.

One of the great things about AA and SÁÁ in Iceland is that they have been instrumental in removing the stigma associated with alcoholism. Just about everyone here has a family member, or knows someone, who suffers from alcoholism and who has received treatment, and thanks in large part to those two associations, this is no longer taboo. People can get sick leave from work to go to rehab, and many prominent Icelanders are, and have been, very open about their struggles with the bottle.

34
BEER: THE DEVIL'S MEAD

Mind you, the Icelanders' efforts to combat the alcohol problem have not always been so effective.

A few decades back, Icelandic authorities felt that a good way to keep the Icelanders from killing themselves with the sauce would be to ban beer.

To ban beer.

The logic ran something like this: The Icelanders are hopeless alcoholics. They will drink themselves into a stupor on any given evening. Come morning, they will naturally want the hair of the dog, ergo *beer*. If we give the Icelanders beer, they will drink it like soda pop, and will be locked forever in a vicious cycle of alcoholism. So we'd better just let them drink hard liquor, to save them from themselves.

Er ... yeah. It doesn't take a rocket scientist to spot the holes in that argument. To exacerbate the problem, in the early 1980s a new fad gripped Iceland: that of English beer pubs, the kind that offer draught. Beer pubs sprouted like mushrooms. The only problem was that there was no beer to put on the taps.

But the Icelanders don't die without a plan, as one of the more succinct Icelandic idioms puts it. They came up with the ingenious idea of mixing light beer (what the Icelanders call pilsner and which is around two percent alcohol) with hard liquor (the wicked *brennivín*, or just plain old vodka) and putting it in kegs to be served on tap. And so you got Nicelanders hanging round down the pub, drinking a concoction of liquor and pilsner so foul that it made your stomach churn ... but in proper beer mugs.

Not sure whether this was the tipping – or should that be *tippling* – point, but a few years later, on 1 March 1989 to be precise, Icelandic authorities abolished the beer ban and set the Icelanders free to drink themselves to death – on beer.

35
ON BEING *FLOTT*

The Icelanders are such a strange mix of the cosmopolitan and the provincial.

They're amazingly well informed about current events and what goes on in the world, generally well-travelled and educated, techno-savvy, connected, and trendy.

Yet they can also be terribly insular, small-minded and nepotistic.

Keeping up with the Joneses is a national pastime in Iceland. There is enormous pressure – overt and covert – to keep up appearances and be *flott* – a word that lands somewhere between "cool" and "awesome".

This means keeping up with your neighbour in the trend sweepstakes, which by extension means wearing the latest fashions, having the coolest hairstyle, buying the most expensive furniture, owning the biggest car, possessing the most Iittala trinkets, having all the latest gadgets ... basically conforming to whatever Icelandic society deems most desirable at any given time. Bucking the trend does not happen much

in Iceland – the social pressure to conform is just too intense.

The flott syndrome rose to unprecedented levels during the boom years in the first decade of this century, when the oligarchs who eventually brought Iceland to the brink of bankruptcy outdid themselves in their efforts to be flott. So much that the flott turned in on itself and became un-flott. Yachts, helicopters, private jets, washed-up pop stars hired to perform at parties, homes in exotic locations, escorts, sordid tales of debauchery… things that, on looking back, just make you go *ick*.

In fact, one of my favourite words in the Icelandic language is one used to describe that kind of situation: *flottræfilsháttur*, made up of the words flott, *ræfill* and *háttur*. Flott, of course, means flott, ræfill means derelict or bum, and háttur means manner. So flottræfilsháttur essentially means to be flott in the manner of a derelict. Like "tacky", only smellier.

36
RAISING THE
COMPLICATION
LEVEL

Being flott also extends to things like social gatherings, which tend to become exceedingly complicated in the hands of the Icelanders.

Where I grew up, if you wanted to throw a party it was a pretty simple procedure. You basically just let your friends know there was a party at your house and that it was BYOB. Then you threw some chips in a bowl (or if you were feeling especially fancy you cut up some veggies and made a dip, or had cheese and crackers), put some music on, and waited for everyone to arrive.

Similarly, if you wanted to invite people for dinner, you'd maybe invite them over for a barbecue, and everyone would

bring something to throw on the grill, plus their own bottle of wine. You, as the host, might make a salad and supply the baked potatoes. The main idea was to *keep it simple* because that was what generated the most incentive to actually get together.

The Icelanders' motto, on the other hand, seems to be *make it complicated*.

For example, if the Icelanders throw a party they feel really weird about making it BYOB. They consider it their responsibility to supply all the booze for everyone. And chips in a bowl is unthinkable. The food served at the party has to bear witness to some serious kitchen prowess; it has to be *flott*.

Meanwhile, an Icelandic dinner party will almost always consist of a three-course meal. Often there will be different wines for each, carefully selected (and supplied) by the host. None of this making-a-pot-of-chili-and-throwing-it-on-the-table scenario that I recall from living abroad.

Incidentally, I should mention that even though hosts usually supply the wine, bringing a bottle along to an Icelandic dinner party is always appreciated and will most certainly garner you a few extra points with the person throwing the party.

37
INVASION OF THE FOOT MASSAGERS

Icelanders adore the latest trends, fashions, styles, gadgets. If it's new and hip, the Icelanders will love it.

Which is fabulous up to a point. I mean, what's not to like about being hip and cool, right? The problem starts when materialism runs amok and people start mortgaging their grandmother's house to buy that new Lexus. And the Icelanders have been known to run amok on occasion. I'll say no more.

Never has this little character trait been more spectacularly evident than in the era of the turquoise foot massagers. Back in the 80s, electric foot massagers shook the Icelandic nation to its impressionable little core. They were the new *hott* gadget. The object du jour. The standard for hipness. The benchmark of cool.

The lure of the turquoise foot massagers was impossible for the Icelandic nation to resist, and that Christmas they sold like gangbusters. They were, hands down, the Present of the Year.

Within two weeks of receiving the coveted massagers, however, pretty much everyone had figured out that they were little more than cumbersome plastic tubs with a bottom that moved

back and forth, back and forth, back and forth, ad infinitum.

And that is how practically every other Icelandic storage room wound up containing a clunky electric foot massager. Those puppies have been emerging one by one ever since, finding their way into Salvation Army stores and Red Cross markets – a blazing turquoise emblem of the Icelanders' susceptibility to marketing and the most banal form of peer pressure.

38
HOUSE PROUD

Having a beautiful, comfortable home is one of the most important things in life for the typical Icelander. Comfortable because, given Iceland's climate, they spend so much time indoors, and beautiful because they spend so much time indoors *and* they need to keep up with the Joneses.

When an Icelander purchases a home, be it a house or an apartment, moving in will almost always involve extensive remodelling. Many people cannot imagine moving into a place without gutting it first and installing all new fixtures – kitchen, bathroom, flooring and such. The impulse to want to have the latest and finest – just like your neighbour or sister or

colleague or best friend – is overwhelming for some, who feel hopelessly inadequate if they can't install that hot tub, or fireplace, or Italian marble countertop, or massive sectional sofa in the latest colour and fabric.

One testament to this passion for decorating is the Facebook group Skreytum hús, which literally (and oh-so prosaically) translates to: "Let us decorate a house". In that group, scores of Icelanders solicit advice on decorating projects, and proudly share their before and after pictures – though only if the "after" is a resounding success (curiously I have yet to see a post where the undertaking in question was a monumental failure). The Skreytum hús group is so popular, in fact, that at last glance it had nearly 60 thousand members. Keeping in mind that the population of Iceland is a mere 350 thousand, this means that roughly one in every six Icelanders has joined. Skreytum hús has become such an institution, in fact, that one of the largest Icelandic paint store chains has developed a full range of colours in honour of the Skreytum hús group, and offers special deals and discounts to its members.

Outlandish as this may seem, perhaps we shouldn't snicker at the Icelanders for wanting to have trendy, comfortable homes. After all, the Icelandic nation spent centuries living in turf huts, with limited light, hardly any ventilation, and the residential quarters built above the cowshed for warmth. Indeed, there are still people alive today who vividly remember life in such abodes. So maybe the hankering after a bit of luxury is simply built into the nation's genes, like so much else.

39
OF BIRTHDAYS AND BIG BIRTHDAYS

Where I grew up, if it was someone's birthday it meant it was their special day and they'd get special treatment. Friends might bring a cake over, or take them out for dinner, and the idea was that the birthday person would relax, have fun and feel pampered.

In Iceland, it's the opposite. When someone has a birthday, it is their responsibility to provide the best sort of experience for their family and friends. People don't take you out for dinner, you take *them* out for dinner. And nobody bakes you a cake (unless you're five years old). That's your job.

Having a birthday in Iceland is not for the feeble.

It's particularly not for the feeble when it comes to the Icelandic *stórafmæli*, literally "big birthday" – the ones that end in 0. Stórafmæli parties are super lavish, and the most lavish of them all is the 50th birthday bash.

In many instances the stórafmæli are too big to be held in people's homes, so banquet halls are required. The guest list

will usually incorporate the extended family, friends, co-workers and spouses. Guests turn up at the party in their best attire, bearing generous gifts, and the birthday person will see to it that there is plenty to eat and drink. Needless to say, everything will be super-flott. There will be speeches, friends and family will get up and tell amusing stories about the birthday person, and there may well be a running slide show of photos from every part of that person's life – the sillier, the better.

Needless to say, throwing such a bash is a pretty hefty proposition financially. However, like a wedding, the stórafmæli are regarded as events to remember for a lifetime, and as such may be regarded as entertainment investments for the future.

40
THE INGENIOUS QUOTA SYSTEM

The Icelanders have an amazingly effective quota system.

No, it has nothing to do with fisheries management, though they *do* have an OK system for regulating fisheries, meaning they calculate how much of any given species of fish is swimming in the sea around Iceland and how much of it can be caught for the stock to remain sustainable. They then issue quotas on how much fishing can be done. This has spawned its own set of social injustice, mind you – but that, as they say, is another kettle of fish.

No – this quota system of which I speak is of an entirely different nature and concerns how long you can say hello to someone before you have to say hello to every single person you run into when you're walking down the street.

Let's say you meet someone in a bar, and you have a long,

drunken conversation in which you go on about how your first husband/wife cheated on you, and how your kids are cooking crystal meth in the garage, and how you just had your lips done because you must adhere to a certain beauty standard otherwise you won't be taken seriously at work.

And then you run into them in IKEA a week later and you say "hi!" and "how are you?" (unless you went a tad too far in the disclosures, in which case you would hide inside the nearest kitchen display) and you have a little conversation. Then maybe you run into them a month later on Laugavegur, and you say "hi!" and "how's it going?" and your conversation is a little briefer. And as time goes on, every time you run into them the hi's get a little less enthusiastic, until they're maybe down to just a nod. And then one day you run into that person on the street and they just look right through you.

And that will be because the quota has expired.

Pretty ingenious, right?

In my experience, a typical quota lasts for around 18 months. Maybe two years, depending on circumstances. After that, you're back to being strangers.

41
HOWEVER, IF YOU ARE OVERSEAS …

The quota system is suddenly retracted, or no longer applies.

If one Icelander runs into another on the street abroad, they will greet each other like they are long-lost cousins, even if their quota back home expired long ago.

Also, when Icelanders live abroad and hear of other Icelanders living in the vicinity, they are delighted and cannot wait to make their acquaintance. Even if they are really "not your type of people" and you would never associate with them back home. If you are living abroad and they are living abroad they are automatically kin because they are Icelandic. The main ingredient in this kinship will be that you speak the same language and that you have the same background. Even if you don't.

Example: when I lived in Germany, I was instantly embraced by the Icelandic contingent there, even though I was, effectively, a foreigner back in Iceland. I had not grown up there, I was socialized as a North American, I had not really lived in Iceland for decades … but I spoke Icelandic and so it was assumed I was from the same background. Of course the truth surfaced when I stared blankly at people when they made certain cultural references or told stories from back home. But it didn't matter. My genes, and especially my understanding and command of the language, were enough.

Then bizarrely, when I moved back to Iceland, I ran into some of the people that had been involved in the Icelandic community in Germany and they looked right through me. Evidently my quota had got lost en route back to the homeland – or maybe it was just that so much time had lapsed. In any case, it was clear that the "we-are-all-Icelanders" credo did not apply in the Land of the Ice, the way it had in the Land of the Lederhosen.

42
HOW DO YOU LIKE MY INSECURITIES?

The Icelanders are supremely proud of their achievements and exude an aura of great confidence on the global stage. They also suffer rather horribly from small-nation complex, also known as "How Do You Like Iceland" syndrome.

Legend has it that Ringo Starr, as he prepared to step off the plane on his first arrival in Iceland in 1984, was accosted by a reporter who thrust a microphone in his face and asked breathlessly: "How do you like Iceland?" To which a bewildered Ringo naturally replied, "I only just got here".

Ever since, "How do you like Iceland" has been the quintessential phrase representing the Icelanders' obsessive need to know what the external world thinks of them, and to constantly seek validation from outside.

A prime example is when someone famous comes to Iceland. The visit will most certainly be reported in all the Icelandic media, with the subtext of how fortunate we Icelanders are that someone so important has deigned to set their illustrious

foot on our humble ground. That person will then instantly be dubbed *Íslandsvinur*, or "friend of Iceland", a tag that will follow them for the rest of their days whenever they are mentioned in the Icelandic media. Íslandsvinurinn Justin Bieber. Íslandsvinurinn Ed Sheeran. Íslandsvinirnir Beyoncé and Jay-Z. Oh, and Íslandsvinurinn Brad Pitt – never mind that he only spent an hour or two in the Keflavík Airport Air Terminal while his plane was refuelling.

Similarly, anything about Iceland in foreign magazines or newspapers makes headlines in the Icelandic media, to the effect of: "Look! *Time* wrote about us!" And anyone with any sort of clout overseas, be it a professor from Harvard or a member of the EU parliament, who makes any sort of remark about Iceland, is instantly revered and hailed as the latest Íslandsvinur.

Not that this is all bad. The upside of the small-nation complex is that Icelanders tend to be open to listening to those who may have something valuable to pass on – and most people do listen with great interest. Whether those recommendations or suggestions are then followed up on is another matter entirely, for as we know, if there is one thing that characterizes the Icelanders it is their aversion to following anyone else's rules but their own.

43
IT'S A FAMILY AFFAIR

Icelandic society is very close-knit, and family is of prime importance. This goes for both the immediate and extended family. Important rites of passage like birthdays, christenings, confirmations, graduations and weddings revolve around the family to a large extent, and friends or "outsiders" are rarely incorporated into that circle.

Obviously this family orientation can make things really difficult for people who move to Iceland from other countries, especially if they don't have an Icelandic partner. Those who do have Icelandic partners tend to get incorporated into that partner's family; those who do not often feel like they are on the outside looking in, since they are not really admitted into the inner circle of Icelandic life.

This is very different from, say, North America, where I grew up. There, families tend to be spread out more. With the absence of family, friends become very important. In Iceland, the family is almost always within easy reach, so the community of friends that tends to get created in other countries

doesn't really carry the same weight. Family is always number one.

Big occasions like Christmas and Easter, and various rituals like christenings and confirmations, are usually family affairs and do not involve friends. Single adults who do not have families of their own will almost always be incorporated into the extended family, spending Christmas with parents or the family of a sibling, for instance.

Not to suggest that all Icelandic families are bastions of joy and harmony – far from it. Iceland has some seriously dysfunctional family dynamics, just like every other place. However, it is rare for people in Iceland to completely dissociate themselves from their families. Even if they are at odds, they will usually try to work things out, or simply grin and bear it, because being removed or "excommunicated" from the family is such a big deal. It's hard to find the kind of support that the family usually provides in Iceland outside the family circle. Icelandic society just isn't set up that way.

As a result, assimilation can be a lonely and difficult process for foreigners in Iceland who are not automatically incorporated into a family. Icelanders have no need, really, to open up to newcomers – and if the truth be told, they probably often find it a tad uncomfortable. Just like the lady who rented me that apartment years ago, they like to have people around that are, well, just like them. Meaning: people who are indoctrinated into the customs and mores of Icelandic society.

Personally I take my hat off to any foreigner who decides to stick it out in this country without an Icelandic partner or family. That being said, associations like the Society of New Icelanders, or Facebook groups like Away from Home and Living in Iceland, have made a real difference in providing networking and support for non-Icelanders, which is invaluable, even for those immigrants who do have access to family but occasionally need to detach and associate with other expats. Because as those of us who have had the expatriate experience can testify, it is sometimes a question of maintaining your sanity.

44
ON CONVOLUTED FAMILY TIES

Icelanders are big on the family – but boy, can those families be convoluted.

Icelandic families tend to be cobbled together from different parts (my children, your children, our children). Often this is because it's no big deal for kids to be born out of wedlock. In

fact, many people "accidentally" have one child at a (relatively) young age, then go on to educate themselves, meet their life partner or whatever, and after that proceed to start a family.

Children that are born out of wedlock are almost always welcomed into the families of both parents (except in some very dysfunctional cases) and have the normal sort of access to grandparents and so on. All sides of the different families then show up for birthdays, graduations and the like. In fact, a child will sometimes have three sets of families – the family of the parent s/he grew up with, the family of the parent s/he didn't grow up with, and the family of the new partner of the parent s/he lives with. All together at the child's birthday party.

As in other Western countries, the divorce/separation rate is pretty high in Iceland. People divorce and remarry and some-times do it again, and then they've got a trail of stepchildren, which does sometimes get confusing. Especially if those step-children have children and you get "grandparents by way of ex-step-grandson" kind of relations.

And with convoluted families come complicated emotions. Broken families often mean broken hearts – that's the same all over the world.

45
EMBRACING BABIES

With all that focus on the family, it should come as no surprise that there is some serious pressure in Iceland to have children. "Childless by choice" is not a common maxim in the Land of the Nice.

"*Á ekki að fara að koma með barn?*" (Aren't you going to have a baby soon?) jovial relatives will ask unabashedly at family gatherings. Or, if the woman or couple has only one or two: "*Á ekki að fara að koma með annað?*" (Aren't you going to have another soon?)

I once knew a woman in her fifties who was unmarried and childless. She said she had never experienced any stigma around not being married, but loads of stigma around the fact that she didn't have children. Which I think pretty much sums up the attitude towards those two facets of life in Icelandic society.

Whether it is this pressure that accounts for the fact that Iceland has one of the highest birth rates in Europe shall remain unsaid. Yet one thing is sure: if it takes a village to raise a child, Iceland is about as close to a village as you get in the Western Hemisphere. For one thing, children blend seamlessly into Icelandic society. The sort of sharp division between

children and adults that you see in many Western societies, where children are more or less relegated to the suburbs, does not exist in Iceland. Children are everywhere, and they are welcome. Indeed, one of the first things that struck me when I moved back to Iceland with a three-year old was how many establishments, like banks or shops, had special corners for children, where they could play, watch videos, or similar, while the parents went about their business. And most Icelandic adults speak to children as individuals – not just as little people that should be seen and not heard.

Iceland has something else invaluable to parents: the aforesaid close proximity to family. Most people – though certainly not all – have family members nearby who are ready, able and willing to help out with the kids. It's a normal part of life. Most people take it for granted that their parents or siblings will be there for them, and they usually are. No matter what challenges the parents face – single-parenthood, heavy workload, full-time education – they'll usually be able to rely on their families to help out.

Plus, Iceland is safe. You can still send your kids out to the store or to the playground without being afraid that they'll get abducted by the bogeyman. Icelandic parents realize this, and value it greatly. In fact, it's a deal-clincher for many Icelanders who decide to move back home when they start having kids, even after living for years abroad.

All that being said, Iceland is not some kind of glorious utopia for raising children. It has many of the same problems as

elsewhere – limited places in day-care, ridiculously underpaid childcare workers, parents who struggle to balance work and quality time with their children, etcetera. And yet, at the end of the day, most Icelandic parents wouldn't want to raise their kids anywhere else – old aunties at family gatherings notwithstanding.

46
SNOOZING IN THE OPEN AIR

A long-standing tradition by which many Icelanders swear is letting babies nap outdoors in their prams. Some folks will even have two prams in use – one for walking with baby, and one (usually an old model the parents have borrowed somewhere) for keeping on the balcony so the baby can sleep in the fresh air.

This is believed to strengthen the child's constitution. And short of leaving their children outside in a hurricane, Icelandic parents *will* place their children outdoors for their nap – come rain or shine. All warmly ensconced in their

lambskin-lined pouches, tucked behind a nylon net or blanket to keep out leaves, snowflakes or other stray matter.

This image of prams with sleeping children in them, parked outside cafés while the parents sit inside, happily sipping lattés with their parenting cohorts, has become one of the more iconic representations of Iceland in the foreign media. As such it has been severely criticized by people all over the world.

Not so much for the fact that the babies are sleeping outside, but rather the implication that Icelandic parents are both careless and delinquent to leave their precious offspring outdoors and unsupervised in this manner ... even if those same parents are sitting right on the other side of the window pane from the perambulator in question.

Be that as it may, the Icelandic nation – made up of individuals who I venture to say were nearly all made to sleep outside in their prams as children – received some shocking news a few years ago. A study just-then conducted reported that Icelandic babies who sleep outside in their prams may suffer some serious oxygen deprivation as a result – specifically due to the blanket or closure draped over the opening of the pram (to keep out the snow and flying debris).

This unnerving information spread through Icelandic cyberspace (read: Facebook, Icelanders' social media channel of choice) as quickly as lice infesting the heads of kindergarten children. Icelanders suddenly found themselves questioning the wisdom and validity of this established national strategy for producing hardy kids. Even worse, they wondered what the exact manifestation of this oxygen deprivation in their own case might have been. Could it explain their ADD? Their social media addiction? Their commitmentphobia? The fact that Iceland had never won the Eurovision Song Contest? No one really knew, but it was a thing worth pondering ... until they couldn't be bothered anymore, and moved on to their next concern.

47
ON CONFIRMATION.
OR SHOULD THAT BE
CONFORMATION.

Religious confirmation is one of those important rites still very much entrenched in Icelandic society, though over the years it has become devoid of much of its original meaning. Initially a deeply pious affair that marked a young person's induction into adulthood, over time it has morphed into a sort of materialistic free-for-all to rival even Christmas itself.

The confirmation takes place in the year when young people turn 14 and is officially a rite of passage to confirm their christening. The confirmation children show up in church to declare before a minister, God and their families that they accept and are willing to abide by the religious doctrines that were thrust upon them as infants. An entire winter of religious teachings is involved, culminating in said ceremony.

Afterward there is a reception, often held in a banquet hall

but sometimes at home, which is attended by the entire family (immediate and extended) and family friends. These are almost always very lavish and can range from an afternoon gathering with hot and cold refreshments, to three-course sit-down dinners replete with speeches and live music.

Guests who attend a confirmation reception are expected to bring gifts, which nowadays mostly involve cash (often wryly referred to as the price of admission). Meanwhile, gifts from parents or others close to the confirmation child are typically expensive and may include laptops, plasma TVs, queen size American beds, overseas language courses, or horses (the live kind), all depending on the parents' solvency. Three or four decades ago, a typical confirmation gift from a parent to a child was a new watch, or a Bible. Not so today.

Confirmations are a major economic force in Icelandic society each spring. The trappings are endless. Confirmation children must have a completely new outfit for the event and have their hair done in one of the latest hairstyles. After the confirmation ceremony there is frequently a photo session with a professional photographer. The reception, of course, is a chapter unto itself, with its lavish set-up, decorations and food service.

It stands to reason, then, that anyone hoping to profit from the confirmations advertises like there is no tomorrow. Banks, photographers, catering companies, bakers, florists, clothing shops and anyone else even peripherally invested will go to great lengths to promote their services. Some of that

promotion even takes the form of direct marketing by snail mail and includes the name and address of the confirmation child that the company in question has managed to procure: *Dear confirmation family, Now that Jón's big event is imminent, we would like to make you aware of* ... and so on.

Many people find the hypocrisy surrounding the confirmations a bit much and instead opt for secular confirmations – also a popular option for those who, for one reason or another, were never christened by an ordained clergy. These are offered by a humanist organization and are similar to the religious confirmations, except that instead of the religious indoctrination, kids learn about relationships, ethics, feelings, human rights, equality, adult responsibilities and so on.

The secular confirmations, it should be said, are rather looked down on by some of the more bourgeoisie Icelanders, who consider them pseudo. I can recall at least one of my daughter's friends wanting to opt for the civil confirmation, but eventually bowing to the pressure of the family matriarch (the grandmother), who simply would not allow it.

48
ON GRADUATION

Another important rite of passage in Iceland: the graduation, especially the matriculation from upper secondary school.

Until recently, most Icelanders graduated from this educational level at the age of 20. Upper secondary school was comparable to senior high school and the first two years of college in North America, or A-levels in the UK. Those four years between elementary school and matriculation were important to people on so many levels, not least because Icelanders tend to form friendships during that time that last for the remainder of their lives (and have sometimes led to heavy cronyism and corruption in the political sphere … but that is another story). In 2015 that term was shortened to three years on the grounds that Icelanders who went to graduate school abroad were almost always two years older than their foreign peers. With the shortened term of study they would only be one year older, which would almost certainly make *all* the difference to their social adaptation. (Not.) Call me a cynic, but I'm inclined to think that the other reason commonly cited for this change was the real dealbreaker: the shortening of upper secondary school means that graduates enter the labour market a year earlier and therefore have a full extra year to engage in

profitable work, leading to more money in the state treasury.

Whatever the prevalent argument, the decision to shorten the upper secondary level was exceedingly controversial – and I can understand why. Though I was not in an Icelandic upper secondary school myself, I have observed how very important those years are to the socialization of most Icelanders. The education they receive is so much more than academic. Most upper secondary schools have extremely vibrant extracurricular activities. They also compete with each other in various pursuits, though interestingly it is rarely in sports, as is often the case elsewhere. Probably this is because of Iceland's climate, which in the past made outdoor sporting activities impossible during much of the school year. Instead they compete in such fields as musical talent, debating, and general knowledge. In fact one of the most popular programmes on Icelandic television is a quiz show running over several weeks every winter and spring, where Icelandic upper secondary schools vie with each other for the national championships, with one being eliminated each week until the end.

To sum up, the years in upper secondary school are both formative and very important to the majority of Icelanders, and the graduation from that educational level is a major rite of passage, marked by a host of rituals and traditions.

On the day of the graduation there will be a formal ceremony, either at the school or in some external auditorium. Prior

to that, students will have gone out and obtained themselves a special white cap that the Icelanders call *stúdentshúfa*, or "student cap". The principal of the school gives a speech, there is the handing out of awards, and the school *dúx* – the person who has the highest overall grades that year – is announced and praised. Finally, when all traditions have been observed, the principal invites the students to put their hats on all at once, which they do with a flourish and to a big round of applause from the audience, which is made up of their families and friends.

Following this there will typically be a photo session (professional photog required, of course) before the *stúdent*, as he or she is now officially called (this refers to the fact that they've graduated, not their ongoing process of studying, as it would in some other parts of the world), heads to wherever their graduating party is being held. Sometimes this will be in a banquet hall, sometimes at home – but wherever it is, there will almost always be plenty of food, beverages, celebration and – sometimes – singing involved. With so many friends graduating at once, the *stúdentar* eventually head out on the town where the merriment continues long into the night – of course with everyone still wearing their white student caps. Then, a couple of weeks later, most stúdentar will head off on a trip with their fellow graduates to someplace sunny and warm, where the party continues non-stop for about two

weeks, usually much to the chagrin of the local hotel operators. By then the hats have usually been parked atop a bookshelf or dresser back home – a proud testimony to its owners' recent accomplishment.

49
ON MARRIAGE

Still another rite of passage: the wedding.

In Iceland, it is unusual for people to take the traditional dating-courtship-engagement-marriage-children route. In fact, many Icelanders do it backward – first they have a child (or children), then comes the engagement, and finally, say, when the children are old enough to act as ring-bearers, the wedding.

Until fairly recently weddings were utterly passé in this country, with people just shacking up forever and not bothering to tie the knot. But then winds shifted, as winds do (especially in Iceland), and big, fluffy, white weddings came back into style. And when something comes into style, the Icelanders will scramble all over each other to get on board.

So now when an Icelandic couple wants to make it official (in a church and everything, not just via their relationship status on Facebook), there will first be a stag party for the guy and a hen party for the girl – though the Icelanders prefer to associate it with another type of poultry and call it *gæsun*, to "goose" someone. These goose parties can be pretty hardcore and far removed from the blithe wedding showers you get in, say, North America. To wit: if you happen upon a guy wearing nothing but a diaper and sunglasses and standing in the middle of Lækjartorg square singing "I'll Always Love my Mama" by the Intruders, chances are that you've stumbled on a stag party. Or if you see a woman wearing a feather headdress and parading down Laugavegur in a corset and tights to the tune of "I Will Survive" or similar, it's very possible that someone is getting goosed.

Either that, or it's the Gay Pride parade.

Come the nuptials, irresponsible antics are far behind and we're in traditional mode. Like elsewhere, it is usually the role of the father to walk the bride down the aisle. The traditional wedding reception after the ceremony will usually involve a rented hall or similar, copious amounts of food and drink, and slurred, drunken speeches. At some point during – or after – the party, the bride and groom will head off to spend their wedding night somewhere nice. Assuming they can get a sitter.

In the morning, the groom generally gives the bride a *morgungjöf*, literally "morning gift", probably a throwback to

the idea of a woman being a virgin until her wedding night and being properly rewarded in the morning as a result. Which is pretty hilarious, since there are probably few places in the world where "saving yourself for marriage" is considered less important than in Iceland.

50
ON DYING

Icelandic death rituals are pretty fixed and are adhered to by the majority of the population. Which I suppose makes sense: when someone close to you passes away, the last thing you want is to be bucking convention.

When someone in Iceland dies, the relatives of the deceased usually solicit the services of a minister, who attends to them throughout the funeral preparations and procedure, taking into account their specific wishes and needs.

This is assuming the funeral is to be held in a church, mind. In some cases it will be conducted by a humanist organization that also offers secular confirmations, christenings and weddings. This is not common, however.

Funeral services are almost always open to the public, meaning anyone can attend. In rare instances they are closed affairs – generally if the family of the deceased cannot afford the sort of funeral that in Iceland is considered proper, if the deceased person has requested a private funeral, or if the family has decided to keep it discreet for whatever reason.

Assuming the funeral is done the traditional way, there will generally be an open casket ceremony about a week or so after the death took place, open only to the immediate family and those who were close to the deceased. This is a very private and intimate affair and anyone who is not part of the innermost family circle will attend by invitation only. The ceremony is held in a chapel, as opposed to a church, and the service is conducted by the minister who also conducts the subsequent funeral service. He or she will usually say a few words, and then those in attendance are given the opportunity to approach the casket and say goodbye to their loved one.

This open casket ceremony is, in my view, such an eminently civilized and compassionate affair. It is also so very Icelandic. The Icelanders have a saying: *Að bera ekki tilfinningar sínar á torg*, meaning "You don't parade your feelings around in the town square". Most people find it exceedingly uncomfortable to show strong feelings in public. The open casket ceremony gives those who were close to the deceased an opportunity to come together and say goodbye privately. They can then display their true feelings in a safe setting, among people they

trust – taking the edge off their grief before putting on a brave face for their more extensive network of friends, colleagues and peers at the open funeral service.

That service is usually held a couple of days later. Traditionally it will be announced in the main newspapers and sometimes also on the radio during a special series of announcements known as *Dánarfregnir og jarðarfarir*, literally "Death news and funerals".

The service is typically quite formal and incorporates the minister reading an obituary describing the person's life, as well as passages from the Bible. There will also be choral singing and/or classical music recitals. The full service normally takes 30-45 minutes, and when it is finished, about eight pallbearers who were close to the deceased carry the casket out of the church and into a hearse. People mingle outside and express their condolences to the relatives, after which the hearse drives to the cemetery, followed by anyone else that wishes to go along. The closest relatives always do, and once there, a short burial ceremony is held. The minister says a few words, then people move in procession to the open grave and make the sign of the cross over it, sometimes also dropping flowers onto the coffin.

Immediately following the burial, those who went to the cemetery head to the reception hall, where there will be a lavish repast, and where those who chose not to attend the burial

will be waiting. This is known as the *erfidrykkja*, the funeral reception, and it is an important part of the funeral service. The sombre mood tends to lift when people who each had their own unique relationship to the deceased come together, and the erfidrykkja almost always provides a great sense of comfort to the bereaved.

Cremation, meanwhile, which traditionally has accounted for a very small part of Icelandic burials, has recently been gaining in popularity. In such a case the casket is removed from the church and the immediate family proceeds directly to the erfidrykkja. The cremation ceremony then takes place later.

A description of Icelandic funeral rites would be incomplete without a mention of the *Morgunblaðið* obituaries. *Morgunblaðið* is Iceland's longest-standing newspaper – and has, if truth be told, fallen into rather ill repute of late, as it is owned by the country's fishing moguls, Iceland's version of Big Business Corp., and edited by one Davíð Oddsson, who many view as being the architect of the Icelandic economic meltdown. Be that as it may, *Morgunblaðið* stands unrivalled in its *minningargreinar* – the obituaries that, to the Icelanders, are such an integral part of saying goodbye.

On the day of the funeral, the minningargreinar – literally "memorial articles" – about the deceased run in *Morgunblaðið*. These take the form of a short obituary with a picture,

followed by articles about the person that can be written and sent in by anyone, and which are published free of charge. These can be incredibly emotional – I cannot count the times I have sat all teary-eyed over my breakfast, reading a minningargrein about a complete stranger.

Predictably, the minningargreinar do not necessarily give the most accurate picture of the deceased person – they are usually heavy on the flattery and decidedly non-critical – but they are a tradition that most Icelanders would not want to do without. Most significantly they show that, in Iceland, everyone matters. Whether you are a president or a homeless person there will almost certainly be a minningargrein about you in *Morgunblaðið* when you die. Someone will always remember you, and care enough to write about it in the paper.

ABOUT THE AUTHOR

Alda Sigmundsdóttir is a writer and journalist, and the author of
several books about Iceland. She was born in Iceland and raised in
Canada, which accounts for the fact that this book is written in a
combination of British and American English. (Sincere apologies to
anyone who might find this disturbing.) Alda has written extensively about Iceland for the international media, and is a frequent
commentator on Icelandic affairs. Catch up with Alda on her
website aldasigmunds.com, where you can also sign up for her
monthly newsletter, or find her on Facebook, Twitter and Instagram.

Other books by Alda Sigmundsdóttir:

The Little Book of Tourists in Iceland

The Little Book of Icelandic

The Little Book of the Icelanders in the Old Days

The Little Book of the Hidden People

Icelandic Folk Legends

Unraveled - a Novel About a Meltdown

Living Inside the Meltdown

THE LITTLE BOOK OF THE ICELANDERS
© Alda Sigmundsdóttir, 2012

Second Edition

Little Books Publishing
All rights reserved

Illustrations: Megan Herbert
Cover design: Emilía Ragnarsdóttir/Forlagið
Layout: Erlingur Páll Ingvarsson

ISBN 978-1-970125-00-9

**LITTLE BOOKS
PUBLISHING**